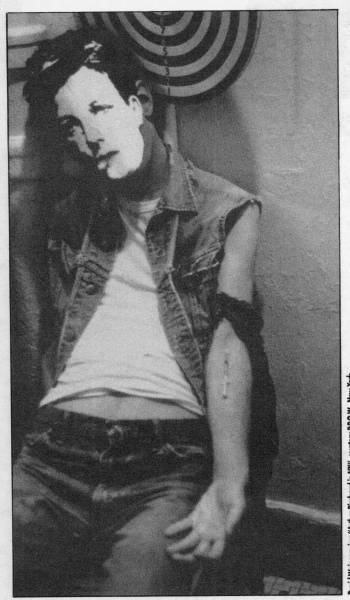

David Wojnarowicz: "Arthur Rimbaud in NY", courtesy P.P.O.W., New York

HIGH RISK 2

WRITINGS ON SEX, DEATH, AND SUBVERSION

Edited by
Amy Scholder and Ira Silverberg

NEW YORK / LONDON

A CIP record for this book can be obtained from the British
Library on request

Introduction and Collection Copyright © 1994 by Amy Scholder
and Ira Silverberg. For permissions see page 365

First published in 1994 by Serpent's Tail, 4 Blackstock Mews,
London N4

Phototypeset in 11/15pt Janson by Intype, London
Printed in Great Britain by Cox & Wyman, Reading, Berkshire

CONTENTS

CONTENTS CONTINUED

Acknowledgments

Many thanks to all the writers who submitted work to us. And for their support, thanks to: Kathy Acker, Dorothy Allison, Pete Ayrton, Wanda Coleman, Dennis Cooper, Katherine Dunn, Peter Ginsberg, Tim Gleason, Essex Hemphill, Edward Hibbert, Rachel Klayman, Zoey Kroll, P.P.O.W., Tom Rauffenbart, Assoto Saint, Harold Schmidt, Lynne Tillman, David Trinidad, and always Rex Ray.

In Memoriam

Craig G. Harris
Bo Huston
Felicity Mason
Tede Matthews
David Wojnarowicz

INTRODUCTION

Amy Scholder and Ira Silverberg

IN 1989, WHEN WE started working on this book's predecessor *High Risk: An Anthology of Forbidden Writings*, the culture world was hard hit by increasing instances of government censorship. We saw writers holding back their more transgressive work in response to this repressive atmosphere. Self-censorship became as much of a threat to challenging writing as any restrictions from the outside. We put together *High Risk* to provide a forum for work that might otherwise have been overlooked.

The first volume of *High Risk* was published in 1991 and received support from an array of readers and critics. It introduced thousands of people to writers, some of whom had never been published widely, whose visions were as diverse as they were outspoken. *High Risk* included stories on such topics as masochism (a guy nails his dick to a piece of plywood); alternative medicine (a man with AIDS cures himself by drinking his own piss); masturbation (an abused girl escapes harsh realities through autoerotic bondage); and coming of age (a suburban teenager learns about sex when she fucks her best friend with a toothbrush). We presented work that was provocative, funny, irreverent, weird and, always, literary.

High Risk 2 assembles work by twenty-two new contributors. The stories, poems, and essays deal with AIDS and mortality, urban violence, sex for money, sex for drugs, sex for revenge, sex for sex, suicide, and sensationalism. Although censorship of the arts may not be making headlines as it was in 1989, it is still difficult for challenging work to reach a wide audience. We know, however, that an audience exists, and we hope the diversity of the writing in *High Risk 2* parallels that of its readers.

What struck us most as we put together this book was the understanding that many of the contributors are preoccupied with death, mortality, suicide, and the disintegration of the body. Like the first volume, *High Risk 2* contains a lot of writing on sex. But what is central here is sex's relationship to death: in some cases morbid, and in some cases, elegiac.

Well into the second decade of AIDS, a sense of loss and grief permeates our culture, but we're not all dead yet. Here are some perverse, and some profound, ways of looking at the world today.

Amy Scholder
Ira Silverberg
June 1993, San Francisco

I'M GOING TO GO OUT LIKE A FUCKING
METEOR!

Craig G. Harris

*The worst of it is that I may not have seen the worst of it,
that today's horror may be tomorrow's
as a candle is to the sun, and the sun to a supernova.*
— *Craig A. Reynolds*

IT IS A BEAUTIFULLY warm Monday afternoon and I wake with good spirits to receive a telephone call from a former colleague in Washington, D.C. We talk about my current situation, I crack jokes in the face of adversity, and we laugh hilariously like old times. After a few minutes, she tells me that someone is waiting outside her office, that she must run but had just wanted to holler at me for a second. She tells me that I haven't changed a bit and that she loves me. She'll keep in touch.

Today is the last day I can remit my rent check without penalty of a five percent late fee. I find my checkbook and cringe as I write the check. When I signed the lease, almost two years ago, I knew full well that the rent was outrageous. But now, my hand shakes a little more nervously each month as I sign the check.

I take the check to the management office on my way to the corner bodega. I notice that somehow I have only a one-dollar bill in my wallet and realize I must stop at the automatic teller machine before I can buy milk, juice, and butter for breakfast. Two twenties are ejaculated from the machine along with a receipt. The record indicates that the current balance of my checking account is only four dollars more than the amount of the check I have just given to my property management. That doesn't worry me as much as the fact that my savings account is at a zero balance, and payday isn't until Friday.

I head to the bodega. I buy a pint of half-and-half, a can of mandarin oranges, a pound of butter, a can of papaya nectar, and a pack of cigarettes. I hand the Arab woman behind the counter a twenty-dollar bill. She packs my groceries and hands me six dollars change. I stare at the change in my hand thinking that if I could really get around like I used to, I could have gotten a better bargain at Balducci's. Small matter. This place is grossly overpriced, but it is convenient.

By the time I return to my complex the mail has been delivered. My life has become so solitary that I am forced to look forward to this daily ritual. As I relock the box and peruse the envelopes, I am overjoyed to find that today's assortment contains two reimbursement checks from Blue Cross-Blue Shield.

I return to my apartment, pour my first cup of coffee, and sit with a cigarette to open the good news. The checks total $325 – an amount I have already paid my therapist and hematologist. This will carry me through the remainder of the week. I open the next envelope, which is a $380 bill from my radiology oncologist. After reading every word on the bill three times, I conclude that these fees cannot be billed directly to my insurance carrier as I had been led to believe. I must remit payment and then submit a claim for reimbursement. The worst of it is that this bill only covers the cost of two radiology treatments and I receive four treatments per week. I lose my appetite and decide to skip breakfast, though I know quite well that my body is in desperate need of the vitamins and nutrients, calories and bulk. Six hours later I read the bill for a fourth time and realize that it can be submitted directly to Blue Cross-Blue Shield. By this time, however, I have missed two meals and spent the day in a depression. I sit and contemplate my situation. I am one of the lucky ones. No matter how unfortunate my situation may seem, I know that I am a "privileged nigger." I know this because not only have I worked every day of my life, but for the last seven years I have worked in various positions in HIV prevention and service delivery. I have a good job. I have health insurance coverage. I have access to the most updated medical information and a stellar medical team. In no way could I compare my case to that of Evelyn, a former client.

I met Evelyn shortly after returning to New York in the spring of 1988 to assume the position of executive director of the Minority Task Force on AIDS. Evelyn had been diagnosed with lupus in addition to HIV disease. She was trying to shake a drug habit, was only somewhat literate, and was dependent on social services. Her man had left her to marry another woman. She had a five-year-old son, but couldn't depend on the father for child care because his wife was afraid the young boy would infect her infant. Bureaucratic systems both baffled and intimidated Evelyn.

4

Like most progressive activists, I had a conceptual handle on social injustices, but I had never encountered them firsthand, until the day Evelyn came into my office sobbing, interrupting my work on a grant proposal which, if approved, would allow the Task Force to add to its overstressed staff of two. Evelyn explained to me that she had no money, her food stamps had been cut off, and no one at the local welfare office could explain why.

I called the welfare office, explained my position, and politely asked to speak with a manager. That request was initially denied by the surliest public servant I have ever encountered. She told me Evelyn's food stamps had been discontinued because she was "too stupid" to know how to fill out the forms. I informed her that I would be happy to send someone to the office to pick up the forms. I would then complete the forms for Evelyn and have them returned by the close of business. The clerk told me they didn't operate that way, I couldn't push through the process, and Evelyn would have to make an appointment later in the month to pick up the forms.

I realized it was now time for me to demonstrate my trilingual roots (I am fluent in Anglo, Afro, and Homo). "Look, girlfriend," I told her, "I run this muthafuckin' agency and I would strongly suggest that you go find someone in a comparable position at yours quick, fast, and in a hurry because you're dancing on my last damn nerve and your office is only nine blocks from mine. I will not hesitate to jump into a gypsy cab and before you can blink, suck your teeth, and roll your eyes and head, I'll be whipping your ass all up and down a Hundred and Twenty-Fifth Street." Within moments a supervisor was on the line and the situation was corrected. Nonetheless, when I returned home that evening I cried at the day's events, knowing there are a lot more Evelyns out there who do not have advocates for their cause.

On January 29, 1991, my hematologist informed me of my diagnosis of pulmonary Kaposi's sarcoma. He compassionately explained to me that I would probably have to undergo aggressive chemotherapy treatments for several months. When I complained, he explained that the most recent studies from San Francisco indicated that if someone with my condition was left untreated, his average postdiagnosis life expectancy was three months. He ordered blood tests, X rays, and a gallium scan. On the way home, I stopped at a liquor store and purchased a bottle of Haig & Haig Pinch Scotch. I also stopped at Li-Lac Chocolates and purchased a pound of champagne truffles.

Back at my apartment, I poured myself a drink and placed a half dozen of the chocolates on a china dish. I surveyed my mail, payed bills, renewed my subscription to *OUT/LOOK*, and proceeded to conduct my personal business. I played back my telephone messages and copied the numbers of callers onto a message pad. I had received a call from my friend Lauri, with whom I cochair the African American Alumnae/i of Vassar College.

Positioned with my Scotch, chocolate, cigarettes, and Vassar file, I returned the call. Lauri and I discussed pending business, divvied up assignments, and made lists of the items we would fax to each other the next day from our offices. With all business efficiently taken care of, the conversation became more social.

"So, how are you doing anyway?"

"Okay, I guess. But my doctor diagnosed me with AIDS today. Pulmonary Kaposi's sarcoma, more specifically."

"What? And you let me go on like that about business? Why didn't you stop me?"

"Well, you know, the shit has to get done and life does go on."

After I finished talking with Lauri, I started to make a few obligatory calls to inform people of my condition. The first call was to George, with whom I have worked on these issues for many years. I suppose that's why I expected him to react to the news in a more enlightened, professional manner. George listened to the details and then asked me what I was doing. I explained to him that I was having cocktails and eating chocolate. He told me that I was in denial.

"No, I'm not in denial. I just told you, I'm drinking Scotch, eating chocolates, and I have AIDS. That's not denial, George."

I firmly believe that every individual has the right to select a support group that works for him or her. Mine, for the moment, happened to consist of Benson & Hedges menthol lights, twelve-year-old whiskey, and expensive confections. Without them I don't know how I would have made it through that first night. With them I managed to call my brother, some cousins, and assorted friends, realizing that each time I'd have to assist them in dealing with their issues before they could assist me in dealing with mine. Disclosure is a very tedious task.

After completing the calls, I turned on the television set hoping to find something other than coverage of the war in the Middle East, which our country had entered into thirteen days earlier. I had no idea that I would find President George Bush delivering his State of the Union Address. It seemed as though he talked forever about the wonderful job the troops were doing in Kuwait. He insisted upon referring to Saddam Hussein only by his first name, which he consistently mispronounced. He tried to assure us that adding to the devastation in the Persian Gulf was what made the United States a great country.

President Bush dedicated only a short portion of his speech to domestic issues. Somehow he managed to work AIDS, illiteracy, and homelessness into one sentence, and indicated that the government really couldn't solve these problems. But he suggested that U.S. citizens become a thousand points of light to tackle these dark, despairing social ills, and recommended that each American visit a person with AIDS.

I was too plucked to get angry. I turned off the set, thinking to myself, Darling, the last thing I need right now is company.

Feces, or the lack thereof, figure prominently in my life these days. As for others infected with HIV, shit has become a friend, a confidant, a significant other, an adversary, an enemy, and a nemesis. It is rarely a source of pleasure. Recently, it has had an almost liquid consistency and burns vehemently upon exit – leaving my rectum with a sensation similar to what I felt on those occasions when I attempted to accommodate suitors who were larger than life.

The rotation of chemotherapy drugs (doxorubicin, bleomycin, and vincristine) which I receive weekly may be the cause of unrelenting constipation or uncontrollable diarrhea. I must schedule events according to these side effects with little advance warning. On several occasions, I have had to forgo parties or dates to go dancing because my bowels were so incredibly constipated that it caused severe pain in my abdomen and back, making it difficult to walk or even stand for an extended period of time. At other times, warnings of upcoming diarrhea have caused me to reschedule appointments, calling ahead to say that I'd be late. On these occasions, I have sat on the toilet with a book, counting time by the quarter hour and carefully investigating anything that lands in the lavender water so that I will be able to report it to my physicians.

Yes, my shit has become something I study. My shit has become an anticipated activity. My shit has become a topic I have had to learn to become comfortable discussing with my service providers. My shit is no longer a private matter. In fact, my shit, at times, has gone quite public.

A few weeks ago, after a relaxing weekend, I spent Monday morning and afternoon at the computer, taking care of other business from my home office. I organized all my files and computer disks with the intent of stopping at my office between my six-thirty cobalt radiation treatment and my eight-thirty therapy appointment. Preparing to go into the city, I showered and dressed in a Senegalese suit. I looked in the mirror and found it to be one of those days when I felt somewhat good about the way I looked, despite weight loss and skin imperfections. As I boarded the PATH train at about five forty-five, I thought to myself that my timing, so far, was pretty good. I was pleased that I had completed a great deal at home and should have just enough time for printing, Xeroxing, and transmittals between appointments.

Between the Pavonia Newport and Christopher Street stations I felt a churning and heard a bubbling in my abdomen. First I thought it was just gas. That happens quite frequently. Then I panicked, remembering that as often as not it is impossible to distinguish gas from pending defecation until after the fact. Then it happened. I felt the mass of shit filling the scant space between my hips and cotton briefs – a feeling of outrageous discomfort, not particularly because of the tactile sensation, but rather because of the social awkwardness.

Situations such as this really challenge one's problem-solving abilities. I exited the train station at Christopher Street, then thought this was a poor choice because of the potential number of friends and associates I might bump into in that area. Thoughts flashed quickly. I stepped out of myself in order to address myself in the second person.

"Take a taxi home . . . You can't take a taxi to New Jersey, you only have two dollars in your wallet . . . Get to a bank machine . . . No, don't use the one at Sheridan Square, you'll definitely be spotted there . . . Use the Chase on Eighth at Twelfth, no one is ever around there . . . Check yourself, is it showing through? . . . That's a shame, you just got that suit out of the cleaners . . . Okay, honey, you're at the bank, it's gonna be okay . . . No, no, take out more money . . . Yeah, eighty dollars is good, that will get you out of this one . . . Now, find a nice restaurant that will let you use their men's room . . . Clean up . . . Hide the soiled briefs in paper towels before you place them in the trash can . . . Find a discount store on Fourteenth Street so you can get yourself a new pair of underwear and a washcloth . . . Okay, so they didn't sell washcloths, you got the underwear, you're gonna be okay . . . Call your radiology technician and see if she'll wait . . . She won't wait? Oh well . . . Take a taxi to your office, it's late enough that almost everyone is gone . . . Sit on one hip in the taxi, and tip well . . . Smile really friendly at your office's security guard, they'll never suspect anything . . . Beeline it to the men's room . . . Take your time to wash up more thoroughly . . . Change into the clean underwear . . . There, that's better . . . Now, go salvage the rest of your evening, honey, 'cause you haven't even seen the worst of it."

11

I went to my desk, printed from my computer files, Xeroxed, addressed envelopes, read my mail, etc. I completed all the tasks I had planned. Then I took a taxi to my therapist's office. I didn't talk about the incident. We spent the hour discussing other issues. After all, with how many people do I have to sit and chat casually about my shit?

During my second visit to my hematologist, he prescribed a number of medications. Aside from the antiviral, Retrovir, I was instructed to purchase Myambutol tablets, Zovirax capsules, and a five day supply of Vepesid oral chemotherapy capsules. I went to a nearby pharmacist who had been recommended by my physician, hoping he would assign the costs to my insurance carrier.

When I presented the prescriptions to the pharmacist and asked about assignment, he explained to me that he couldn't do this with Blue Cross-Blue Shield, but that there shouldn't be a problem. If necessary, I could write a check. Thinking to myself that I don't possess any major credit cards, carry a New York State driver's license but live in New Jersey, and have no identification that bears any reasonable resemblance to my current blond bombshell look, I figured there could be a problem with the acceptance of my check.

The pharmacist packaged the drugs and used an electric calculator to tally the costs. When he reached the balance, he looked up at me with a smile and said, "Mr Harris, that will be one thousand, three hundred and twenty-nine dollars and fifty-five cents. Oh, and you can postdate the check."

Thirteen hundred and twenty-nine dollars! And I can postdate the check? Until when?

I picked my chin up from the counter and nervously wrote the check. The lack of identification wasn't a problem. The pharmacist explained to me that he didn't have to see any ID because he was fully aware that my doctor didn't "see riffraff." But what if I received medical attention in a clinic or emergency room? What if I didn't have health insurance coverage that would reimburse me eventually? Thirteen hundred dollars for four prescriptions – and this was only the beginning.

*

HIV has totally warped our perspectives on sexuality – both individually and collectively. Without a clear understanding of safer-sex guidelines, so many people have adopted the practice of celibacy (which frequently manifests itself in drunken or drug-induced forays into unsafe sex that are lamented the morning after) or the limiting of sexual partners on the basis of medically unsound criteria ("He looks healthy," or "He's an upstanding member of my church"). Despite increasing rates of HIV infection and venereal diseases, no one I know is having sex, or at least they're not talking about it. I'm no exception.

In the winter of 1988, I was finally able to dissolve a lover relationship. During the three years that followed, I spent a great deal of time contemplating what had gone wrong, and why the relationship had lasted much longer than it should have. I've concluded that at age thirty, I was determined to settle down, and that I had enough false confidence in myself to believe I could make that union work. But the fear of intimacy, codependence, lack of commitment, political differences, and poor communication were too much to overcome.

The question I have asked myself most about that relationship is why I tolerated so much for so long. In the past my basic rule was one strike, you're out. I think it had to do with laziness. It is a real chore to acquire and maintain a loving, working relationship in the age of AIDS. Fear of HIV and its related prob-

13

lems have entered every recess of our consciousness, constructing even more barriers than those which already existed for gay men of African descent. The stamina to keep searching, to keep trying, is very difficult to muster. More frequently, I am inclined to agree with the lyrics of an old Merry Clayton tune, "Love me or let me be lonely."

Entering into a conversation with each new sexual partner regarding one's personal interpretation of safer sex and sexual boundaries is a very emotionally loaded situation. One usually reveals one's personal sexual history, political viewpoints, medical knowledge, fantasies, and fears. Of course, communication need not take the form of conversation, and in certain situations (baths, tearooms, parks) such talk would be totally inappropriate. In many anonymous sexual situations, actions speak much louder. But in dating situations, the silence around such issues is noticeably deliberate.

Since my diagnosis, I have shared details of my health with two men whom I am attracted to. The initial news of my illness and subsequent updates have been met with compassion and consideration. Both of these men have been a major part of my support system, offering varying levels of affection. But I have not had sex with either of them. At least, I don't think I have. One of the strange things about this era is that we interpret sex very differently now. Is a sexual act defined by penetration? orgasm?

In any case, six months of celibacy is not fun. But rather than push harder to solidify either of my two existing relationships (neither of these men is looking for what I am looking for within a relationship), or seek other suitors, I try to satisfy myself with video lovers who don't ask questions, don't shy away from the intricate details of my body's malfunctions, and don't tell me during intimate moments that they are really having difficulty dealing with my "terminal illness."

This approach is not without its merits. When I become fatigued in the middle of the act, I can push a pause button on the remote and resume activity at any time. I do not have to fear exposing my body and its multiple lesions. I do not have to have arguments about why I decided not to take my medication this morning. I do not have to explain why the soreness of my rectal tissue will not allow penetration.

On the other hand, I haven't been held tightly in bed for four months. I haven't been able to curl up with my back against another's chest and feel his arms around me. I haven't been awakened by a light kiss on my eyelashes. I haven't shared a bath, or received a massage from someone who cares for me romantically. My sex life has been sanitized far beyond the impact of the intrusion of latex props.

I do not feel lonely. There are always enough telephone interruptions, cards, and even occasional floral arrangements sent by friends. My family has been there for me constantly, offering support, money, transportation, and hands to hold during medical procedures. My many friends are good to me. But I still feel alone.

15

I feel alone on Friday nights when I want to celebrate making it through the seven medical appointments of the week. I feel alone on Monday evenings when I stop at a flower stand on the way home from my therapy. I feel alone when I am pleased with a new poem or essay I have just finished but there is no one I can turn to immediately to share these words with. I feel alone most of all when I realize that through the years I have become stronger than would have been necessary if I had had a shoulder to sob on, arms that reassured me, lips that passed on a reason to live.

I want to live the rest of my life, however long or short, with as much sweetness as I can decently manage, loving all
the people I love, and doing as much as I can of the work I
still have to do. I am going to write fire until it comes out of my ears, my eyes, my noseholes—
everywhere. Until it's every breath I breathe. I'm going to go out like a fucking meteor!
—Audre Lorde, A Burst of Light

I'm not waiting for a cure. I'm not looking for a miracle. I am not resisting the inevitable. I will die. I will die much sooner than I would like to accept, and there is little I can do about this fact. Kübler-Ross can call that acceptance if she wants, but in doing so, I believe she minimizes one's will to fight. It is precisely because I know I will die that I work even more diligently for the causes I believe in.

It is within this framework that I make decisions about my medical care. It is within this framework that I have made decisions to increase my activities or lessen my involvement in certain organizations. It is within this framework that I continue to plan and conduct HIV prevention programs for African American gay men. It is within this framework that I renew my commitment to work on a manuscript of poetry and fiction that I began over two years ago.

It is all about the quality of life. And I find that quality of life is a control issue. I refuse to be controlled by a daily regimen of oral medications and radiation therapy. I refuse to be controlled by weekly chemotherapy treatments. I refuse to be controlled by the increasing number of side effects. I refuse to be controlled by fatigue or depression. I refuse to be controlled by medical bills or reimbursement checks from my insurance carrier. I refuse to be controlled by limitations imposed upon me by my race/ethnicity, class status, sexual orientation, and health status.

I have made a commitment to relinquish control only as a last resort. Until that time, I want to live the rest of my life with an energy that ignites and irritates, burns and bubbles, soothes and inspires, until it bursts from this atmosphere, dissipating into the cosmos.

THROWING SHADE

Darryl Pinckney

I DON'T HAVE DROP one Puerto Rican blood. My people were butterscotch nigs from Georgia. My father got stationed to Puerto Rico for forever. He acted all day like his ass was pre greased and when he came home be having these black outs and wet the couch. My mother raised Dobermans for the dog fights. She had nine at one time once, the mother motherfucker and eight baby motherfuckers almost grown. My father went out back one night with his .45 and took those motherfuckers out. Dog brain on the wall and dog paw hanging on the fence. My mother be putting orange juice in with the eggs and flinging tears, talking about how she knew she was never going to get the fuck off that island. We got twisted off her scripts. I can speak Spanish but I don't like to.

I wasn't born in Puerto Rico but some fabulous tit was. I love my tits because I raised them. Both my tits my children. I was nineteen and I had just got fired from this piece of job at Save Rite in Atlanta. The manager call me a freak. I was fem but all I had then was brown wavy hair. It was down to my waist. I put it up under a hair net and the manager call me a freak. So I painted my nails and went on hormones. Then I went back down to Puerto Rico because my grandmother in Atlanta was bugging behind what I was into. My family goes, Get out, so I came on up to New York.

My father handed me cold cash to get out and never come back. I bought a hundred blouses. They go, Get out, and want to put me through all kinds of changes but I paid them no mind. I always took care of my own self anyway. I'm 32 now and look 21. I weigh the same now I did then almost. I'm naturally chubby in the face so I don't show adam's apple. I don't color my hair to get it light. I used to do Sun-In but it started balding me on top. My hair is a little fine on top so I take some Dippity-Do for bounce but do not, I repeat, do not come upside my head with no hot comb.

I may not be real but I can make money. I never wanted to cut off my T. That would be way too fierce and expensive. I tuck and my trade's nice and quiet. Pull it back and tape it up. I look so real I have to use the Ladies Room everywhere. I sit down to pee. Most tricks don't have idea one because I do blow jobs in cars and where nobody can even think about flatback. I uncover my top and let him feel me up there. I talk and work it, get out the car and go. I do cash up front, they do shoot in the j-hat. Before they even wipe up I'm around the corner putting a little face back on. The others that suss me out get off on it and come by regular. We go to my crib when I have a roomie that won't give shade. Most regulars want attention and get high and maybe some head before they dash. I may not be real but I make them treat me like a lady because Miss Rita doesn't play.

In New York I never had a crib just mine. I must have moved a hundred times and every time I let stuff go. When I first come up I had suitcases, then Red Apple supermarket bags with hardly no handles, then I had the clothes I had on and the Kleenex in my bag and that was it. I was living with my cousin and her husband for a while over on East 23rd Street in The Bertha. Some New York buildings feature Kiss My Ass names like Eldorado Terrace but this was The Bertha. The Bertha had too many Dominicans in it for me. My cousin and her husband was couriers. They carried these little flight bags everywhere, always going to the airport. I think they flew money around but I stopped hearing half the bull they tried running on me because they weren't nothing but small change. Cynthia Citibank was after meat day and night. Game on Cynthia Citibank and she will fuck somebody up quick. I don't mess with banks.

For a while I worked at a phone bank because I have such a sweet and soft voice. Call people up and ask them silliness. I could work night and I liked that but no money. Then I had a job from home with this gay sex line. They call these ads in *Burger Boy* and *The Manhattan Review of Unnatural Acts* and all the ads be leading back to me. I could be fifty trips a day. I could do fem, prep, homie, spic, chicken from Daffey Duck, Kansas. I didn't like rough because the S and M I was supposed to be saying was too funny. I was so down with my voices the job gave me sore throat. But I could talk gold shower and cook dinner at the same time.

Then it got weird with my cousin. She started throwing shade, talking about how everybody could tell I wasn't real because of my feet. I do not have big feet and my hands is small. I was young and didn't know what time it was so my cousin could give me shade. I got into Mandrax and unplugged the phone and passed out in the bath tub. The apartment flooded and then the apartment downstairs flooded. I was out two days and the super couldn't get in because my cousin had these serious locks up and down the door. Every time she got her period she bought herself a new lock. They tried to take the door off but they couldn't do it. When my cousin got back and opened the door water flowed down the hall and down the steps. Her husband, he goes, Do a fade. She put him up to it and he was so pussy whupped he would go along with anything she want. My cousin put me out and she the family I had got along with. She used to come down when we were kids and we be up in my mother's mirror plucking our eyebrows and painting back. I had Rita Hayworth eyebrows by the time I was fifteen.

I used to go to Peter Rabbit down in the Village by the river. I never spent money on drinks in there. Somebody always set me up. They had reefer then but speed was the main thing. I never shot up. Needles is not me. I liked the little green pills with the dividing line in the middle so I could break it in half without crumbling it. This queen's father was a doctor up on Fifth Avenue and we used to get this queen to cab uptown and liberate us clinical speed by the jar.

Peter Rabbit had drag shows Saturday nights but they were lame. Some tired queens moving mouths to Patti Labelle. They used to mop ensembles off the tables and racks on 14th Street and 14th Street was what they be looking like. I never wanted to be in those shows. They gave shade like I held back because I was too mooped to mop but I have a problem with tacky. This gorgeous queen call herself Miss Demeanor could sew and I got a dress off Miss Demeanor one time. It was fierce. I was over. Everybody, they go, O Rita, you look so good. Girl, with what you got you could make some money. I knew I was over but I didn't jump out there right off.

Most queens turning tricks hung out down there by the river or they worked the Westside Highway around Chelsea, out there flipping hair and trying to be grand. They don't make no money except when they take somebody off. I rolled a trick one time. He nodded and I got two hundred dollars. I stayed inside two days. I thought he was going to come around looking for me. He was so fucked up he probably thought he partied and that's why he didn't have nothing left. I scored but I messed up behind what I did because regulars want to count on a girl. He was nice but his breath was like he was throwing up for five years. My first regular date was vice president for a milk company but I had a problem with the territory I was in. It had too many queens. Everybody knows the queens be working it down there and the scene had out some very sick cases.

I went to a base house up on 111th Street way before Richard Pryor burned his pants up and everybody got hip to what was happening. I didn't get high. They must have been passing me a pipe with nothing in it so for a long time I didn't see what doing coke like that was about. I snorted like everybody else. One time I let this white dude fix me up with a speedball. A combination blow and dope. He was in Nam. He had needles in the individual packages. I go, Okay, but I had to look the other way when he banged that vein. I was so looped I couldn't have moved if the house went on fire. The speedball's too fierce for me and I don't like needles. With blow I could keep on the move and all I needed me was a Ladies Room.

The after hours clubs most girls I knew took they money to sold blow right inside the door. Bouncers didn't like people bringing in shit from outside. After hours was buy or fly and the drinks cost seven dollars. But the blow was stepped on, seriously stepped on, cut with sugar, baking soda, comeback, Johnson and Johnson's baby powder. That shit hurt to take it. It was so speedy somebody always go off. I couldn't chill in those clubs. The Men's Room never had door one and the Ladies Room was like a kiddie swimming pool. The toilet water was knee deep because somebody was always trying to flush down something that was just not going to go. Too much was trying to go on and I had to watch my back and watch the bitch that was supposed to be watching my back.

I had a good connect for some blow with these two butch fairies Will Marie and Eddy Jane. I first hooked up with them in Cats at 48th Street and Ninth Avenue. I didn't take it down to the deuce because the heat was too extreme for me to be bothered with carrying my ass around Times Square. One night I'm chilling in Cats and was holding. Will Marie came back from the bathroom and he doesn't give me my tin foil back. I was cool. I invited him. Miss Thing did it all and didn't leave me none. He sees me just drinking my drink like my shit was a memory and he goes, Here, girl. I went and did his and it was the joint. I go,

Where did you get this down biz, Miss Do? He was my ace connect after that.

Will Marie didn't deal outside. People had to call him and ask in code and he didn't let everybody come by all the time. Will Marie and Eddy Jane lived down there at the Hudson Towers on 44th Street with the doorman at the desk, honey. Will Marie was careful about not letting nobody who didn't look right come by asking for him. When I went by I looked very real. Respect the house. I don't paint back anymore. Too much goo is bad for my skin. One time I was on a mission and went and got me a new stem and some Colt 45 and copped and came on back and looked in the mirror and had to fall out. I had been flying around the hood with facial all over me. I was ghost-busting that night. But whenever I went by Will Marie's and Eddy Jane's I came up correct.

Will Marie laid envelopes on the doormen now and then to keep them cooled out but he still didn't want no outrageous traffic coming through his crib. Will Marie didn't like people to cop and then run on out the door. It didn't look right. He'd tell them to sit down. People did lines waiting for Will Marie to give the all clear so it got like a party. It was a good business because when it was cool to make a dash the people had did up what they came to get and had to buy more.

If there was people already up there Will Marie wouldn't do business with me right off. The customers be sitting there with some lines on the glass coffee table and hand me a rolled up bill. Will Marie would shake out a few more lines and we'd kick back. I know how to act. After some conversation Will Marie would let them dash. Then he go get the rock hid in his spice rack and weigh me out direct from that. I don't know where he got yellow rocks but it was the joint most of the time. The coke wrapped up was good but it was more white. I knew he been stepping on it and Miss Thing knew I knew. He had better get up and go find that rock.

Hudson Towers weren't cheap and the crib was high up. They had themselves a telescope and a balcony. Will Marie was the brains. He had a phone sales job from his desk. All I ever saw Eddy Jane do was fry fish and watch *Dynasty*. Will Marie was a snow queen, one of them nigs crazy about white, so all Eddy Jane had to do was have blond hair. Eddy Jane was army. He was supposed to go to Korea his last year in but Will Marie was not having that. Miss Thing carried on until Eddy Jane went and told he was in love. The army put him on a bus. Eddy Jane didn't have nothing to do after that. He had dark circles up under his eyes and watched *Dynasty*. He didn't care. He didn't even care that much about getting high. If the food was out, he eat the food, if the line was out, he'd do up the line, if Will Marie owed the supplier, it be Will Marie that owed.

Will Marie was owing somebody. One time I went by there and the bicycles was history. His shit started to get weak. Another time Will Marie gave me some attitude I did not appreciate, talking about me calling him too late and how I better pay off my tab. I never had no tab. Will Marie was smart but anybody dealing and trying to party at the same time will fuck up. The last time I call up there the phone was off. Eddy Jane be watching *Dynasty* on the curb by now.

I had me a spot in front of this movie house on Ninth Avenue up from Cats. Chat the nigs on the door, take a walk, come on back. It look like I was just coming through to holler at some friends. If the heat was fierce I had this factory badge to put on and broke out a shopping bag like I come off a late shift. I didn't look like no ho in the first place so nobody could say boo to me about what was I doing. I didn't try to turn tricks at the movie. That way the nigs on the door couldn't work me like I owed them. Most of them were winos from way back anyway. They didn't have tooth one and all they could do with T was piss. They knew not to ask me to go to the store for them neither.

One time Lavonnia and her nasty wig ate up my spot. She must have did the manager, this fat white dude with the gold chains, because he told the nigs on the door she didn't have to go nowhere if she didn't want to. The lobby had heaters. It was so cold on the sidewalks it was like something was trying to burn the bottoms off my feet. I hadn't broke night yet and I was out there two hours. Lavonnia had her big hips in some see through pants. I just had my black shawl. This wild boy Lavonnia knew from down the street at the male burlesque trucked by feeling no pain. I seen Miss Thing around but Lavonnia knew every trifling little hustler. She goes, Beam me up, Scotty.

He was pinned and look like a chipmunk. We went with him around to this crib he was crashing at on 46th and Tenth and after he had got in the door he spit out about ten vials. I couldn't see how anybody could stick that shit up in the mouth. No telling what places that shit been before. He didn't care because he was in this nasty sweater be smelling like old come. The only time Dennis the Menace shut up was when he was coming back from copping and had the crack up in his gums like he could swallow his shit if the cops busted him.

He used a empty beer can to smoke with. He turned the can sideways, squashed the can on the top side with his palm, poke little holes in it, put ashes on the holes, put some crack on the ashes, hold a match to the crack, draw on the hole where the tab was, and had himself his pipe. It didn't smell right to me and I kept getting ash down my throat. I didn't like the taste but it was cold out there. I was crashing with this case on methadone be selling her doses from her switchboard job at this call girl outfit, asking me to let her hold ten dollars every time she saw me. I wasn't ready for her so I sat back on the sofa and hung.

It was this old man's crib. Every time after his hit he get up and lean over the sofa and straighten his diploma on the wall. He didn't have nothing else because Dennis the Menace had took him off for everything already. I sussed from the get go how Miss Thing showed up when the old man's social security was making the mailbox and after he had smoked up the man's money he'd book. After the man had got his check again, Dennis the Menace be back leaning on the buzzer downstairs, talking about whose stretch had pulled up at the burlesque waiting for his pimply ass.

The old man paid for the shit but his boy wouldn't let him touch his beer can, holding it for him like he was feeding a baby. They should have checked his lying mouth. He was throwing half full vials back behind the stove. When the old man look at the stove Dennis the Menace wave his donkey dick up in his face like the shit was hid so they had a one on one to get down with later on. I didn't care if he stashed because the crack wasn't getting me. But Lavonnia was mad. She goes, You said you'd do me a solid.

I would have nodded but the old man got this broken off stem somebody must have left there. It was black from somebody trying to smoke the oil from beat shit. The screens was hard and black and he couldn't do nothing with it. Lavonnia goes, Give it here. Get me some alcohol. She cleaned those screens, rolled them back up, and scraped the black off the inside of the stem with the end of a coat hanger. The stem was still good because it wasn't broke except on that one end. She pushed those screens and told Dennis the Menace he had to give her some shit up front because if he didn't act like she was good for it she would have to kick his ass for him.

Lavonnia bit off the vial and slam dunked. She took my Bic, ran the flame around the stem to melt the shit, sucked the flame in at the top, and, boom, Scotty had beamed her aboard. The ho was shaking when she handed me the stem. It was hot and Lavonnia goes, Forget cool down. Hold it up and hit it, girl. I did. Blizzard went up in my mouth. They were screaming not to let it out or swallow it. Smoke was coming out my ears and out my nose. My eyes was crossed and my head be thumping. I had to let it out like somebody punched me. I saw sparks.

We got pinned that night. Dennis the Menace went up to 59th again and the next time Lavonnia and me went with him because she was putting up her only money and the vials he been bringing back was short. The last time we went to cop we had got that old man's rolled up dimes out of a shoebox in his closet. They wouldn't take it like that on 59th and we had to go to a bodega and change them. We didn't leave out of that crib until daylight and Dennis the Menace had on the old man's coat, this brown number supposed to be cashmere not even the Salvation Army would look twice at. Miss Thing was going to spend all day trying to get five dollars for it when he could make twenty in a minute getting hard in a toilet.

I crashed with Lavonnia for a while over in her hotel on 49th near Broadway with no lights on the stairs. The hallways were stinking like lots of dead animals but everybody was too wasted to find the bodies. I didn't know what was laying up in there. Lavonnia didn't have fridge one but the pipes went on in the morning. She didn't need no fridge. Her behind stayed wide enough with the hot dog buns and Debbie Cakes she binged on.

Lavonnia was a garbage can. She want to be high all the time. After she got high she had to come down or die and when her trash be wearing off she had to beam up or kill. She pumped for coke, poppers, black beauties, ludes, reefer, hash, PCP, opium, window-pane, glue, gin, smack, Valiums, laughing gas, coffee enemas. A lot of the time what she got be dirt, tea, vitamins, laxatives, heart pills, muscle relaxers, and she had sucked rat tail to get it. Lavonnia did anybody and not all the time for money. She be spending more time trying to stay high instead of making some money.

I was Miss Chemist. I knew what Scotty was supposed to look like and I didn't mix. I didn't like 59th Street because too many were hanging tough in that cement park by this office building trying to get a p-c anyway they could. They tried to make everybody cop real fast like it was so hot in there wasn't no time to check the shit out. This Dominican with scars on the side of his face was up there. I don't like to speak Spanish but I knew his shit was over because he the one we had gone to with Dennis the Menace. I do not like beat shit. Some people get a little, smoke that up, get a little more, smoke it up, and tip out the door for a little more. That's how they get beat because by morning the straight up pitchers won't be out there. People take they last ten dollars to somebody they don't know and get crank or some poison. I may get a little something when I break night but after that first taste I wait until the man I'm looking for's out there and then I go for the party.

I didn't like to go up there on my own but I got tired of Lavonnia acting like she didn't have good sense. We get up there to 59th and come to find out Lavonnia didn't have dime one. She be running up to everybody, talking about trading head for some shit and I'm holding and suppose to be waiting for her with all these homies moving around on blades. I go, Come on, girl, you know I'm taking care of you. She be on a mission, begging somebody to let her do him with her butt sitting over her rusty heels on the freezing ground. The pitchers didn't want no fat scag going down on them. Even her wig had B.O.

One time after Lavonnia had got herself together and come on out to go to work I tried to hip her word up she had to respect her ass more. She started giving me serious shade, talking about if she couldn't make no money and she had a slit how the fuck did I think I was going to make some money with tits too hard to feel real. Lavonnia was used to a pimp breaking her head for her every night. He had got to the Rock or hell or had cut her loose by that time but she couldn't handle not having nobody kicking her ass for her. If a black Mercedes with no license plate pulled up to the curb and the dude had a ski mask on and a .45 in his lap she would have eased her big behind into the front seat anyway.

I had to step off. They busted 59th Street. I had had me my first heavy night in a long time. I was so thirsty I tipped on down to 34th and Eighth but by the time I had got there it was busted but good, had all the homies in a line the whole block with hands up on the buildings and legs out. I came on back to wait the mess out and laid down on my side of the bed with my gloves on. I had me these black gloves I slept in because Lavonnia would go for loose shit. I put my stem, my good lipstick, and my big money up in the fingers, and kept back two or three dollar in my bag so the bitch would think she be getting something off of me.

Lavonnia fell in the door snotting about she got some bad stuff. She was carrying on and the hotel want to put us out. They go, Take her to Emergency. They came up and took even her shoes out from under the bed, talking about she wasn't paid up and I had no business being in the room. Call me a bull dyke. I had never took my clothes out the locker at Port Authority because I knew how Lavonnia was about anything loose. They go, Put her down in the street.

I had to take her over to St. Clair's. I couldn't get cab one to pause. I had to drag her fat behind three blocks, talking about she can't walk. I sat up in Emergency with her for a hour and she be working everybody's nerves. She worked the desk and the white coats. People were waiting up against the walls and laying out on the floor. Lavonnia lost her seat hopping up. This evil looking home with a bandage up in his chest took it. He goes, Shut the fuck up. I opened a *Seventeen* and looked busy.

Two cops came through with a home dropping in handcuffs. Lavonnia be going for it over there cussing out the nurse just come out the curtain. The nurse must have gave her attitude big time because Lavonnia went off. She goes, Jump back and kiss yourself, bitch. She had that nurse by the hair and off the floor like to snatch her bald. She goes, You can jump back and kiss your ass now, can't you bitch? Everybody screaming and the cops on Lavonnia like white on rice. I got up out the chair, put *Seventeen* in my bag, and made my move out of there real quiet, baby.

Beamers uptown copped on 96th Street from afternoon to the next morning. They jumped off every day at four down Amsterdam to 86th and back up Broadway way past 96th. Manhattan Avenue at 107th was invasion of the base heads no pause. I couldn't get next to a pay phone. They had crews waiting to pick up when the dealers called back. One restaurant at 96th and Amsterdam took Ma Bell out they had so much outrageous traffic coming in and peeing. It didn't work because all the busboys be crewing except this chink buzzard hated everybody but white people.

In the summer half the shit out there in the day time was beat. People in the crack bars want to flash this vial of shit and palm a vial with nothing but soap chips from the other hand. Or they go, I can't bring you. Show me your money and I be right back. They get somebody's money and start flying. I looked for the Colombians on the steps on Amsterdam in the

35

day time. I go, Two, and show my cash. The wife gets slides over to her husband studying his car at the curb. He reach down in the engine or has the shit up in his pocket. The wife tips with me down the street. She goes, Here. Her kids did lookout for the cops. If kids started whistling and singing I stepped quick into a store. One time I dashed off the street into this tax man's office.

The girls on Broadway worked it from 86th to 91st. I could break night in fifteen minutes. I got out there before the other girls woke up. When they came on out me and Nikki be illing over to the projects on 103rd and get a taste from these Nam bloods on the bench. They was always trying to steer us up to the seventh floor but the elevators didn't look right and the stairs was too empty. We let the other girls turn some tricks and after they paused went back out to work. The cars was cruising but the girls had got thirsty too soon. Me and Nikki could clean the street out. Nikki had some serious high heels and one time she was carrying those spikes by the straps. She goes, Girl, my feet hurt. You seen Scotty? Let's go find Scotty.

The Colombian bulldagger didn't pitch until three in the morning. I took my time getting my Colt 45 at this store on 95th because I could scope through the window if Miss Blaster had got to her zone. Every monkey alive be standing on her corner with the cops riding by, waiting to try her for seven dollars, talking about seven was all they had and a gold watch. Miss Blaster didn't want to hear it. A ten saw one of her jumbo vials and ten dollars only. She didn't even like looking at somebody's nasty one dollars. One of her baby dykes took the little money. Miss Blaster stepped off at four sharp. Her babies signal her and she made her move to her van. She didn't care if there was a hundred monkeys following her and waving money. Miss Blaster didn't have to be out there long because her shit was truly over.

I didn't mess with the tag dealers in the basketball court on Amsterdam because they had people getting shot in the head. The homies hanging out in there always want to be acting stupid. The little flavors were giving it up to find Scotty and acting grown like pussy so special when there be fifty of them in there at one time pushing the same fish. Copping from homies late at night was asking to get beat and the Spanish boys were out there on a juice trip because they had Scotty. I look so real Miss Perico came on me like I want to be one of his little flavors, talking about he got what I need.

I was crashing with Nikki in The Crawford on 92nd between Amsterdam and Broadway. It was The Crawl For because nothing but crack heads in there bugging out. This boy's mother was dealing up the stairs from the lobby. Her shit was weak but she was just dealing turn a few dollars into her smack. She had her spoons down there in the cat piss. She had had to cut Junior off because he had fucked her up too many times. Junior got serious behind crack attacks. He got mad and took off her bed. He sold her mattress for a hit and then I seen him a hour later dragging her box springs down the steps and out the door.

When it was too fierce out there we copped on the third floor from this Colombian lola running the business for her son locked up on the Rock. They had kicked out another son back down to Colombia and she was flinging tears behind it, talking about how she was going to do for him. She was so evil I bet she dropped the quarter on her sons herself. Lola made us scope the hall ten times before she reached out the window where she hid her stash. If something went down she was going to send the shit airmail.

We crashed up on the sixth floor in Evelyn's crib. She charged a vial for house fee. Every night Evelyn was crawling over dirty clothes with her skinny Rican ass, talking about a hit she saw fall on the floor. She find paint and popcorn and try and smoke it. She never found nothing. She had tore up the place a hundred times already and even if it was something down there I'm not crawling on my elbows and up in the baby's Pampers looking for it.

Evelyn had two daughters, a baby boy just learned to walk, and sometimes this greasy Rican with tracks between his toes. She be up there with him on the bed pulling and had the nerve to swear she couldn't get pregnant again because she was just faking it for a hit. Evelyn let those children sit up in there all day with the baby banging pans and tasting his own poop. They only had a television because Nikki had got them one. Evelyn didn't care. She was on the steps trying peeling the shit she copped for closet people. Evelyn played on Nikki because Nikki had a son down in Philadelphia with her grandmother. She couldn't go there because of how she looked. Then Nikki caught Evelyn on the third floor after Evelyn had asked Nikki to let her hold five dollars to get some food.

I started pausing at Michelle's on the first floor. She and her uncle the only white people The Crawl For had. Michelle liked to get loud at the kitchen table with her pipe and a big jug of vodka, bulling about the big money a bank was going to hand her when she turned 45. Hers was the only crib in The Crawl For with a bathroom inside so people liked to chill there. Her uncle was in the other room watching television in lingerie. We made him go to the door in his pink robe when we heard Evelyn looking for us.

Michelle played poker Wednesday nights. Nikki brought this regular by on Wednesdays. Nikki was like a model. She could fix herself up and he treated her right. One time he gave her a box of stockings with a rose in the box. Nikki would meet up with him someplace, take care of business, and then bring him back to chill. He liked to get high but he didn't like messing with dealers and thirsty people. He watched *Mary Tyler Moore* with Michelle's uncle and his fluffy slippers. I know how to act but he couldn't stand Michelle's loud ass.

One time Michelle come back early and the man booked. Michelle had lost at the poker. On top of that she couldn't handle this man liking Nikki but couldn't stand her. Michelle started giving shade but Nikki wasn't getting off her shit. Michelle never put money up. She smoke our shit. Call Nikki a skank, talking about how she was going to catch the big A behind Nikki sitting in her tub. Nikki went off and kung fued the door Michelle was trying to put her out of. I go, Later for white trash, but Nikki wasn't having it. Everybody in the lobby was into it. Nikki went out and slammed some iron up against Michelle's window. Then the lookouts started flying.

The cops wasn't just riding by and heard something. Michelle had dropped a quarter on Nikki. Uncle flipped because he had done time. Don't ever call the cops. I stepped across the street and Michelle was lying about Nikki trashing her crib. It was Evelyn took Nikki's bag out to Michelle, going to show the Germans Nikki's butane and pipe. Evelyn already been in it looking for shit and the gas must have been empty for Evelyn to leave it. Evelyn was mad because Nikki had told her she had to take her kids out of there and go back down to Puerto Rico. I had Nikki's good bag. She had handed it to me to hold when she turned and slapped Michelle's pasty face for her. They put Nikki in the car because she was dressed up for a date and Michelle was white.

Undercovers knew what was up and everybody could read them a mile off on purpose. The little Germans been paid off. One Miss Hitler swinging his stuff around I knew was on the take. I seen him tip by a hundred deals out in the open. I was up on St. Nicholas Avenue with a thousand people copping in the rain when the block had a demonstration. These mad nigs were out there with signs and cop escorts. Carmella kept on like it was legal. I didn't know how I was going to get my ass out if something was going to go down for real. They had helicopters up there. I stepped off with the demonstration, marching about take back our neighborhood and my bag be full of the shit.

DQ goes, Why you mess with bottles? He cooked his own shit. Most cookers ran fire directly up under the jar with the water, baking soda, and blow in it. DQ put his jar in a strainer and the strainer in a pot of water and turned the stove up low under the pot. It took half the night for the blow to harden up but his shit was cute. He beeped this dealer for Peruvian flake or sent me and Carmella down to St. Nicholas Avenue. DQ was the cooker so he was too grand to go. They had guns for days down there. They let everybody get a good look. Guns on the tables with the scales and out in the halls everybody was rubbing guns like it was his T. Carmella was mooped the homes wanted to mess with her because she was white Brazilian.

DQ was head chef but the crib wasn't his. It was up on 125th but it wasn't the projects. There were so many hot stereos in the living room it be like Crazy Eddy's Harlem style. DQ looked after the VCRs and televisions for this fence when she was gone. I wasn't supposed to touch them but when I heard DQ at the door I reached over and switched it off. He never put his hand on it to feel it was warm. He had four children down in Miami he hadn't heard of in eight years and been into smack way before he started cooking. I had to watch it because he liked moon rock and I didn't like to be around smack.

Carmella liked running around on a mission, talking about she knew where she could get three dollar vials. Her people supposed to be so rich but she couldn't go by there. Carmella was with her hand out at every McDonald's down Broadway to 72nd. She make nine dollars in change in no time and then move. Carmella had the crack rolled up in this knit cap she had on day and night. One time she took off that nasty cap and I wish her wig hadn't came off with it. Her head was fucked. When she took a hit she hid in the bathroom and got paranoid, begging me to go to the door like she heard something. She hid her stem up under the blanket and then in the cushions. DQ goes, Don't bring that whack shit up here no more. He tried to put her out but Carmella was like a dog kept running back in when the door open.

This one keebler I had was a regular. He paid sweet but I never got a look at his trade because he only want to get high, holding his stem like a cigar and digging in his clothes for a piece he thought fell. He wouldn't let go of his stem and I had a torch and DQ's water pipe. He had smoked a lot of beat shit before and the oil had dripped down. The insides of his hand got brown when his stem heated up and the res started running. It smelled burned up but he wouldn't let me clean it. He wouldn't get himself a new stem neither. I put in new screens for him one time and he be clogging them up with some whack shit.

One time my keebler came by with this ugly four eyed Italian looking girl he lived way in Jersey with. The bitch came in the door with attitude. He was going to have to sell his car because he couldn't pay off his tickets and she wasn't going to let him touch hers. She didn't want to give DQ his house piece, talking about it was her money. My keebler made her give him some shit and he passed it to me. She goes, Isn't Israel in Iran? She was going to sit up there like her conversation was so interesting we didn't mind if she got high in front of us.

Then she smoked up all her money. She had ticked DQ so he goes, I don't give credit. Had it been just us he would have cooked and run a tab. She wouldn't leave and had to be dragged out. She was holding on to the sofa and then the door. She tried to make DQ take her credit cards from this mall down in Jersey for one more hit. DQ kicked her ass out. My keebler didn't care. He knew she needed somebody to slap her face for her. He was nice. When he got his cloud he went upside down on his hands with his Reeboks in the air. He was so fine I gagged. I was so painted about him it was the only time I wanted to fry eggs for somebody sunnyside up like *I Love Lucy*. He goes, I'm not with her anymore. Are you a man? I hope not.

They chased Scotty out of where rich people got tired of it. They bricked up the windows and didn't leave the rats hole one to get into. Broolyn's supposed to be down but I don't do Brooklyn. I had me too many tricks from Queens and Jersey to want to go there. They don't know how to act. I'm not like these space waitresses be looking down and walking real fast like they going to find that lost baggie of crack or that hundred dollar bill before anybody else did. I can make money. I don't need this shit. I'm tired of what shit's good and what shit's whack.

It's supposed to be down up in Washington Heights but there are too many Puerto Ricans up there for me. All that Spanish like a boom box I can't switch off. I didn't come up to New York to do Puerto Rico all over. What's whack is *West Side Story*. When Ricans fight they don't sing and dance. But I have to make some money. If I don't keep my shots up my tits will go away. I'm not ready for my children to go. What's whack is Scotty wanting to play on me and everybody throwing shade behind it. They go, She used to look so good. Miss Rita used to be so over.

STRANGE JUICE
(OR THE MURDER OF LATASHA HARLINS)

Sapphire

I REMEMBER MY boyfriend, the dark behind the brown of his eyes and how he look in his leather. I was walking with that good feeling thinking about him, the next day of school—maybe I go, maybe I don't. You know, who gives a fuck. And nothing special, you know, nothing is so special except now I'm dead. It's the day I died. And the sky was red-brown gauze. You could see patches of blue if you look up but I don't hardly ever look up. My eyes on the ground checking out my feet in orange Reeboks. What else I remember? Now that I look back it seems like the collard greens piled up on plywood boards at the door was huge green tears that tried to warn me. The day was the same but different. I didn't do nothin'. I slid open the glass door of the refrigerator that keeps all the beverages cool, it's so hot here. My eyes glance up at the camera pointed like a gun from the corner of the wall. Fuck it. I slip the cold bottle of orange juice in my backpack, go to the counter. I'll get some gum, if she say something I'll say, aw bitch I was gonna buy this juice, you think I'm stupid.

Wonder what we gonna do in school tomorrow. I be so glad to get out the ninth grade, go to high school. If I'm late for homeroom one more time—

"Oh bitch please! I was gonna pay for—OOG FU WOO SHIT SUE! Speak English hoe! Take your damn juice. I wasn't stealing nothin' from you chink ass hoe!"

She grabbed me. Bitch! I hit that hoe upside her jaw. Who the fuck she think she is putting her hands on somebody. Fuck this hoe, I ain't gon' argue with this bitch. I turn my back. And I walk away. I see the collard greens again only now they're growing like big trees then I see a red dirt road in the middle of the salad bar, no lie, like I'm high or something. Then everything is normal Koreatown fruit stand again. Del Monte corn out of a can poured in a stainless steel tub, iceberg, romaine, bran muffins and brownies wrapped in clear plastic. Fuck it I'm not thirsty no way.

1.

I don't hear the blast till I'm dead
I don't feel nothin' either
as I split in half
a dog yelps
and every sound I ever heard
flies out my mouth on green wings.
Crimson waterfalls open in my skull
and my bones come aloose,

the dog is screaming
like a siren now
and in the distance a bucket of water
spills over on a dusty red dirt road
and my heart quits
falls face first in
shattered glass on a
concrete floor.
The camera keeps
rolling.
My left leg twitches.
I don't cry.
Fifteen.
Green as greens
passing from sight
under broken bottles of light.

2.

I don't remember what I did wrong.
Somebody hit you, you hit 'em back.
She didn't have to shoot me.
I was born here
and someone can shoot me and go home
and eat turkey on Thanksgiving—
what kinda shit is that?
Videotape the bitch killing me,
the hoe's own videotape
recording
the end of my days
reeling obscenely

for tv cameras—
my blood
sweet Jesus!
Rolling 20s
Bounty Hunters
PJs
Imperial Courts
NWA
LAPD
South Central
Hollywood
18th Street Diamond Riders
Easy Riders
it's a brown thing
it's a black thing
Crips
Bloods, Mexicans together forever tonight.
I don't remember . . .
I jus' wanted some juice
and now I'm dead.
Killed by a model minority
success story.
Listen, is anybody gonna
say anything?
I was gonna get a new orange leather jacket
To match my Reeboks.
I was passing math *and*
doing good in English.
Fuck history, I'm tired of hearing
'bout George Washington
and Columbus.

I told that cracker, "Shit, mutherfucker,
what about us?"
No, I *wasn't* pregnant,
but I was gonna have a baby,
definitely, one day.
I like Luther Vandross, Tone-Loc
and Queen Latifah.
Listen, is anybody gonna
say anything?
Community service!
A white bitch
with a pink slit
between her legs
like mine,
drips red.

A white girl that probably got
into law school on the
affirmative action birthed
by black people's struggle,
sitting on a seat
that was opened up
for her by Rosa Parks and
Fannie Lou Hamer,
nig—no, black people, African
Americans, like me, marching
under fire, hoses, broken glass
gasolined bodies
testicles sliced off,
strange fruit, tossed to dogs.
Swinging from trees.

This white judge woman
hooded in mahogany-walled
chambers decides my life
is not worth nothing.
A fifteen-year-old black girl
equals zero in this white bitch's book.
She sentences this yellow gunslinger
to community service and probation.
What are the terms of her probation,
that she don't kill nobody white?
Does anybody hear me?
Without my tongue.
Fifteen and out of time.
Listen to the gasoline on the wind.
50   Listen to my blood rhyme—
drip drop on the sidewalk.
Hear me children—
and BURN.

ONE DAY

Sapphire

All week my period plays at coming
then leaves me bewildered staring
in my panties at faint brown stains
I haven't seen in 30 years.
Is this the end? As it was in the
beginning (brown stains in cotton underwear)
so shall it be in the end?

It never crossed my mind it would hurt—
no long-legged daughters to hate me
or call me old fashioned or outta style
or to say like white girls on t.v., "Gee Mom
you just don't understand," that it
would stretch my heart out
of shape like this, mark my smile
draw such rings under my eyes.
No one ever told me, I never knew
To be part of the counter culture
would be so lonely.

I felt for so long I had to save my own life,
no use in two of us drowning.
And then there was the ABUSE, how it left me
uncomfortable with a naked infant on my lap,
how I was afraid of descending down
to lick the little clitoris or of sticking
my finger up its vagina between diaper changes.
I mean this is what was done to me.

All my life the sound of a child crying
like fingernails raking down a blackboard
twisted something inside of me till it snapped
screaming: shut up shut up SHUT THE FUCK UP!
And I would want to slap, punch, stomp
throw it out the window or in a pot of boiling water—
anything! to get it to stop that
stop that goddamn motherfucking crying!

Then I work.
I work years
in a circle
in a group
in a journal
alone.
I heave, crawl, vomit, abreact, 12 step, psycho-this,
    therapy-that,
anger workshops, homeopathy, crystals—
all on poverty wages.

And I remember
a man so mean

52

so different from the face in photographs
and home movies.
I remember a woman with
red fingernails like razors
up my vagina.
I cry
shake
face the impossible,
write it
tell it.

I can't see any change.
Just all my time, money and
most of my youth spent,
and shelves of books: *The Best Kept Secret,*
Prisoners of Childhood, Kiss Daddy Goodnight,
The Courage to Heal, Father Daughter Incest.
Then one day the woman downstairs,
her with the dope smell escaping
from under the door's dark face,
takes in a baby for money.
And often under the deafening boom boom
of music so loud it sounds like a cannon
being fired I hear a baby crying.

One day it's just a crying and a crying
but instead of wanting to bash its head
on the sidewalk I relax, I relax all over
and a warm pink glow expands around my heart
like in some new age instruction book for meditation,
and I whisper, if that baby was mine

I would just hold it, hold it and hold it, 11 hours
if it took that long, till it stopped crying.
If that baby was mine I say slowly
and see the tiny child body safe in my warm brown
     arms.
If it was mine, I whisper again.
Maybe the baby hears me 'cause the crying
downstairs, in my soul, stops as I hold
my work, the work of a lifetime close to me.

CONFESSIONS OF A GIRL, PART ONE:
THE FATHER

Kate Pullinger

Dead wizards, werewolves, heretics and other outcasts become vampires, as do also the illegitimate offspring of parents themselves illegitimate.
from "The Vampire," *On the Nightmare*, Ernest Jones (1910)

LUCY COOKED HARRY'S favorite dish, the only thing she knew how to make that had garlic in it. Harry had a thing for garlic, he thought it made food taste exotic. She looked forward to feeding him.

But today Harry was late, later than usual. Lucy cleaned the bathroom, tidied her bedroom and then, bored, ventured into Mina's closet and under her bed, but everything was neat, almost pristine, as though the girl did not really live there at all. Lucy opened the drawer second to the top in the bureau which she had bought for Mina when she was a baby.

Outside on the landing Harry paused, his breath short, his heart pounding.

In the drawer Lucy saw birth control pills.

Outside, Harry composed himself and then knocked.

Lucy slammed the drawer shut.

The smell of cooking greeted Harry as Lucy opened the door of her flat. "Ah," he said, smiling, "you've made my favorite." He walked in, stooping slightly.

"You look tired," said Lucy. Harry's face was red and his breath seemed labored. He frowned, it was the wrong thing for her to have said. "That's a nice shirt," she said quickly.

"And you look well yourself," he replied with forced jocularity. "Where's Minnie Mouse?"

"In Paris."

"Paris?"

"Yes. She can get very cheap deals through work and she was so keen, I couldn't stop her from going by herself. She's so independent, you know what she . . ." Lucy paused, remembering the pills. They seemed too real, threatening, a tangible reminder of her daughter's total separateness. Lucy had no way of knowing what Mina did or who she was out there in the world. The discovery of the pills made her feel powerless.

"God only knows the kind of people she meets, gallivanting all over the show like she does," Harry said, still grumpy.

"Well, young people do seem to have a lot of money these days," Lucy replied. She could not tell Harry about the pills.

"I've always said Mina was clever enough to make lots of money." Lucy heard "unlike you."

Lucy carried a pot over to the table, where Harry

had already sat down expectantly. The blood was draining from his face and now he looked very pale. As she served him Lucy noticed he was breathing in short, abrupt gasps. She said nothing and sat down to eat with him.

After dinner, Harry went over to his chair. He was thinking about Mina and how long it had been since she had sat on his knee. Harry missed Mina's easygoing familiarity. It had taken him several years to notice that she had become all breasts and elbows but when he did it came as a shock. Harry did not always make love to Lucy when he came around these days but it was seeing the girl that he really missed. Lucy could sense this and she tried to compensate by being more attentive, even tarting herself up a bit. But Harry was not all that interested. Some evenings he would sit in the chair and look at the door as if he expected Mina to walk through at any moment. But, of course, she didn't, she was always somewhere else these days.

Lucy finished clearing up and then walked back into the sitting room, where Harry was sitting in silence. He looked as though he might have fallen asleep. "Are you feeling all right?" she asked.

Harry jumped, said yes, and then seemed to rally around. "Come here," he said to Lucy, "take your knickers off." Lucy blushed and smiled and did as she was told. She stood in front of the chair and Harry fingered her absentmindedly. She squirmed to stop him from hurting her. Harry looked up at her face as if suddenly remembering where he was. He stood, undoing his trousers. Lifting Lucy's skirt, he put his hand behind her right knee and pulled up her leg. He pushed into her awkwardly, his large belly in the way.

"Do you still want me, Harry?" whispered Lucy. His reply was muffled, his face buried in her hair. Close to tears, Lucy moved her hips slowly. She wished Harry desired her all the time.

As abruptly as he had stood, Harry sat down again. The rough movement of his lungs was audible. He had lost his erection and when he opened his eyes he looked plaintive and afraid. Then his eyes closed and he fell forward. Lucy cried out, grabbed his shoulders, and, when she couldn't move him, ran to the

telephone.

While Harry struggled in Lucy's flat, Mina was fucking a stranger in a foreign city.

Fucking around was something Mina did mercilessly; it was something at which she was skilled. In the early days she had done it by exhibiting a raw hunger so pure that no one could resist. "She wants it. She really wants it," was all a boy could think. With a bit of age and practice her technique had become more refined; now the man always thought it was him doing the conquering. Most men could not even remember what happened, she took that much away with her. All they were left with was a vague memory of her smell; she was not in the habit of exchanging telephone numbers and names.

Bored in the Louvre one afternoon, Mina followed a young French student who carried a sketchpad under one arm. He soon noticed her and they spoke to each other—bad French, bad English. They went to sit outside in the weak winter sun on steps leading down to the Seine.

The boy wanted to be a painter but was studying graphic design because someone had told him it was more practical. Already he was frustrated and a little bit unhappy—he communicated this to Mina through one-word speeches and elaborate gestures. Mina didn't really care what he wanted to do, the way he looked and spoke was enough. He wore a bulky old jumper and very tight jeans that wrapped around his hips handsomely. When Mina put her hand on his thigh he cheerfully gave up his struggle with conversation. They kissed, touching each other through their clothes. On the walk to Mina's hotel they stopped frequently to admire each other and kiss again. Once they had snuck past the porter and were behind a closed door, the young man was willing and eager.

He wants to be hers. He wants her to take him. He opens himself up, bares himself. He won't mind if she hurts him. It is easy.

Mina arrived back from her weekend in Paris and went straight to work. Lucy rang; the words "Harry has had a stroke" sounded oddly familiar. After work,

Mina took a bus to the hospital. She wondered if Harry was going to die.

Stephen felt faint when he first sighted Mina. It was as if he recognized her, although he was sure they had never met. He had gone into a travel agency to book a flight to New York. This time he was going without his parents.

Mina was sitting at her desk. On the wall behind her was a poster from Jamaica. Stephen looked at her and then looked at the picture and only just managed to stop himself from saying something gauche about wanting to lie on a beach with her. He cleared his throat and Mina looked at him. Her eyes had been focused on the door; she was waiting for an important client to come in.

"May I help you?" she asked, and Stephen thought he might die from pleasure at the sound of her voice.

"Yes," he replied, "as a matter of fact, you can. I want to go to New York."

"When would you like to fly?"

"In about a fortnight."

"Just let me see what we've got that might be suitable," Mina replied, pulling out her airline schedules and picking up a pen. Stephen searched his brain for something entertaining to say, something devastatingly witty and urbane. After a few minutes during which he stared at the top of her head, Mina gave him the details. Then she made a phone call, consulting him about dates and times. He signed the forms without asking the price, which Mina then volunteered. "Do you want me to post the ticket to you?"

"No," he said, "I'll come in and pick it up." Mina explained that it would be ready the next week. Then she looked at Stephen expectantly while he sat and stared at her. After a few long moments he stood, banging his knee.

The week between buying the ticket and picking it up passed slowly. When it was finally time to go back to the travel agency Stephen found Mina the same as before: polite, efficient and incredibly sexy. "What's your name?" he asked as she checked the spelling of his. Once she had told him it proved difficult to think of anything else to say. He left the office, ticket in hand, demoralized and randy.

At home Stephen slammed plates around the kitchen, where his mother, Anna, sat reading a book on psychoanalysis. "What's wrong, sweetheart?" she asked absentmindedly.

"Nothing!" he shouted.

"That's good," she replied, looking back down at her book. Stephen continued unloading the dishwasher noisily.

"What are you reading?" Stephen asked after he had breathed in and out a few times.

"Ernest Jones," Anna replied.

"Who?"

"Freud's biographer, another psychoanalyst. They say he was discredited."

"Discredited?"

"He slept with his patients."

Stephen laughed.

Later that night Stephen woke up and, feeling very hot, got up to open the window. As he fell back into a leaden sleep he felt weighed down, almost suffocated with pleasure. The following night he dreamt that way again, coming onto a pillow, the sheets twisted around his body, the curtains blowing wide. And the night after that his body convulsed at the moment he awoke.

He got up and took his sheets down to the laundry room for the third morning running. His mother was at the kitchen table reading the same book. "You *are* fond of clean sheets, aren't you, dear?" she said. Stephen did not reply. He had breakfast and then drove his mother's car to the high street. Mina was there, opening the office on her own.

"I'd like to postpone my flight," he said.

"You'll have to pay extra."

"I don't care."

"Unless there has been a death in the family or serious illness or something like that?"

"No death. No illness."

"What was your name again?"

Stephen cleared his throat noisily. He blushed. She had forgotten his name. "It's Stephen. Stephen Smith."

"When do you want to travel now?"

"Oh, I don't know."

"I'm going in three weeks," Mina said. "You could come with me then."

In New York Stephen did not visit any of his ancient relatives. Instead he and Mina went up in the elevator of the Empire State Building. They walked along Forty-second Street late at night trying to decide which porno cinema to visit. In their gray hotel room with its fluorescent strip lighting they watched the nude talk shows on cable TV.

To Stephen's surprise, Mina would not have sex with him although they shared a bed and did not wear pajamas. She said Stephen had to tell her about himself first—had to confess something which she was unable to guess. Stephen began by reciting his boyhood ambitions from the other side of the bed. He lay on his back trying not to touch himself and said, "When I was really little I wanted to be a teacher but by the time I became a teenager I had decided to be a lawyer but my father wants me to join his business and my mother thinks psychiatry is a better option but I don't want to go back to university and I don't really like any of these ideas at all." He described his father's business and his mother's academic career and when he thought he had probably satisfied Mina's curiosity—he believed that the reason she had asked him to speak was that she did not want to sleep with a complete stranger—he rolled onto his side and in her direction. The silence informed him that she was asleep.

63

In the morning over coffee, eggs, pancakes and hash browns, Mina explained that she had known all those things about Stephen already from the way he dressed, spoke and behaved. He would have to confess something new. They spent the day running around skyscrapers and the sights they knew from countless movies: Mina had never been to New York before. Stephen worked hard to stay calm but had an erection all day.

That night they went to bed drunk. Mina said, "Tell me something." Stephen began by confessing his sexual fantasies, what he wanted to do with Mina if and when given the chance. He could tell she was asleep even before he stopped talking. He began to feel like Scheherazade in reverse, attempting to tell the right story and bring about what he knew must be his fate.

The next morning over a breakfast of muffins, waffles and orange juice, Mina said she was not interested in what Stephen fantasized about but was much more concerned with what he would actually do. They spent the day riding back and forth on the Staten Island ferry and practicing their American accents. Mina was convincing—she could already do Brooklyn, Texas, and Southern California—but Stephen was hopeless. He sounded like his father, Romanian, bits of Yiddish and English all rolled into one.

Later, when they were slow-dancing somewhere dark and smoky, Stephen said, "You know, sometimes I really don't feel English at all. I don't feel Romanian like my parents either. In fact sometimes I hardly feel human. I feel like I've just arrived here from nowhere and I haven't really got a clue what comes next—how to behave, how to respond to life." He stopped abruptly, feeling as though he was sounding ridiculous.

Mina pulled Stephen closer. He felt her breathing; the smell of her hair was at once familiar and strange. She looked up and he kissed her on the lips. Apparently he had said the right thing.

The cruelest thing, Harry thought as he sat in his dark, chilly flat one night after Lucy had left, was the loss of desire. In his chair in front of the television, Harry smoked cigarettes and thought about masturbating. It was humiliating, but having a stroke was humiliating, being in the hospital was humiliating, having to be taken care of was humiliating. Harry had reached the stage where he did not really mind what anyone thought anymore. He ignored Lucy when she came to visit. Death hung about in the eaves of the roof, waiting. Harry sat in front of the television, also waiting.

In New York, Mina had her legs wrapped around Stephen. With her hands gripping his ass, she pulled him forward again and again. She had pillows behind her back; she wanted Stephen to push himself as far as possible inside her.

At first Stephen thought he would not be able to stop himself from coming even before they had taken off their clothes. He felt very hard, the skin on his cock was pulled almost too tight. Mina admired his body—he licked hers, he slid his tongue into dark places and managed not to say anything stupid. She held her body rigid when he first penetrated her; her skin felt very cool except between her legs, where she felt, Stephen thought, indescribable.

In London, Harry was by himself. Lucy had not yet arrived that day. He thought about his life and felt he had accomplished nothing. He felt dissatisfaction and anger. Where was Mina these days anyway?

Falling asleep, Harry dreamed of Mina. She was coming toward him; she was naked and looked more like Lucy than usual. She had blood on her face, her hands, and there was blood spreading between her legs, on her thighs and up around her pubic hair in shapes almost like handprints. "Are you listening, Harry?" she asked.

Harry nodded in his dream, and in the dim light of the room his head moved up and down. "You can't help me now, Harry," she said. "And I can't help you."

In New York Stephen came for the first time, arcing his pelvis into Mina's, fucking her hard, then gently, then hard again. He tried to stop himself—she had not come yet—but he could not. Mina's eyes were open, her hands sliding across his wet back. He rolled off her and curled into a ball.

Harry woke, shaking his head to chase the dream away. He sat up straight. The flat was untidy; he had not noticed before. He stood, and as he stretched, he thought he saw something out of the corner of his eye, something flashing. When he turned there was nothing. Lucy would arrive soon. He took a step forward, he would show her, give her a bit of the old what-for.

Stephen slept a wide-open, happy, tired sleep, his arms wrapped around Mina's tight body. She stared at the ceiling. A fly crackled with electrocution as it hit the fluorescent strip light. Mina felt her soul twist and spin as though it was trying to tear itself free. She thought of Harry. She pushed her bum into Stephen's groin; she reached around and grabbed his thigh. As he woke he found himself with another erection.

67

And then Harry fell. Backwards. He split his head on the table beside his chair, he broke his arm on the chair itself and fractured some ribs when he hit the floor.

In New York when Stephen began to come again, he opened his eyes and looked at Mina. She was crouched over him, her feet on either side of his hips. Her head was turned and she was staring hard in the direction of the wall as she pushed herself against him. She cried out suddenly and said she was coming and Stephen let himself go too. Her body collapsed onto his, her breasts onto his chest, as Stephen felt hot liquid travel through his cock. Mina's eyes were closed and her lips were moving. Stephen could not hear her voice, but this is what she was saying: "May the earth not receive you, may the ground not consume you . . . Are you dead, Harry? . . . Harry, are you dead?"

HUNTERS/
GATHERERS

Stephen Beachy

ENTERTAINMENT

This sexy guy on television tells me the news, his
mouth making slow fellating motions. The news is
death, etc., shivering once and spreading around the
globe in a web of blue electricity: malignant phosphor-
escent dreams crisscrossing the atmosphere. Really,
the news is only death; the "etc." is just the blowjob
I imagine, lips of the sexy image sliding up and down
my cock. The matter of his body has been replaced
in significance by the light which resembles him and
bombards my retina. Meanwhile, the sexy image had
rendered the dream of my own death as another
boring fact. I touch moist underarms, my bellybutton,
pubic hair. He thinks I'm only a ghost, lines in the

air, a dim electromagnetic presence. My dreams aren't any more unreal than his, but have the disadvantage of being tied to my body.

EMPLOYMENT

Walk down to Polk Street, meet a short Caucasian man. Ask for forty bucks, he's only got twenty. Go with him anyway. Outside his apartment are these weird sculpted bushes, so wonder: when was it that a form of organic matter first arranged other organic matter for purely aesthetic effect? Inside, his apartment is full of teddy bears and paintings of people's eyes plus a jar full of non-paper money. Says he has a thing for eyes. Just been reading lots of stuff by this dead French guy about eyes getting gouged out, split by razors, so it sounds kind of sinister. For twenty bucks he expects to get his nipples sucked, plus have a dick in his mouth. It happens for him.

Can you get hard? he asks. Try, baby. Oh, that's right baby, light slaps on the ass.

When we're done I steal a package of AA batteries from his bathroom, to convince myself of something.

The client thinks: what's this boy thinking when he looks at me? Drugged, empty, malleable. None of this boy's observations are true. I'm done, he says, points to the door. Alone, he replays the sex in his head, imagines the boy on the street.

Outside again he enjoys breathing and walking. The sky's filled with chattering bones, like acid trips, strange dreams on cough syrup. All vegetation seems hallucinatory, sort of contrived and artificial. Might make a nice backdrop for sex with fifteen-year-olds: thrusting motions, wiggle of the masculine hips.

Like tons of people he's had dreams about death which involved falling or leaping into flight. He's had dreams about flight which weren't, as far as he could tell, dreams about death. The AA batteries fit perfect in his Walkman: some arty punk drones about the twisted metal and guts of a car crash with lots of cool feedback and grunge. He pictures the soundwaves bouncing around inside his skull, scowls happily.

Downtown, the buildings are huge prison-like mirrors rising up forever. The way seagulls are flocking there must be dead things on the rooftops. The structures of the buildings contain more banal avarice than even the little hunks of hungry meat they spin through their revolving doors. The structure of these buildings magnifies that stuff exponentially. But the buildings are designed to vanish by psychic architects, built from transparent materials. Video art of these instantaneously crumbling buildings could live forever in a perpetual feedback loop. Still, he likes to imagine the buildings themselves burning, makes the sound of explosions (pkkeww pkkeww) as he walks down the street, creatively visualizing ruins and flames.

LOVE

On Polk Street one night at Frank Norris Alley (named not after an astronaut, as some hustlers believe, but after a dead writer) this old Caucasian communist picks me up and buys me a beer. We discuss things. He adores the Kennedys, for example, whereas I only think they're so much wasted matter. He thinks the baseball cap our bartender wears backward is an idiotic symbol of mainstream fascist America. Dude, I say, that's what this culture does: you take stupid symbols from the breeding cult and give them a different context. Ironic or whatever. He doesn't get it. When I use some ridiculous word, postmodern or marginalized or something, he doesn't know why I'm hustling. He wanted a victim of capitalism, without other options. Usually, I say as little as possible. Nobody wants to pay someone to have sex with them who's smarter than they are.

He takes me home, probably to prove me wrong. For someone so old and ideological he's sort of attractive. He used to teach acting at a large, spacious university. We watch an ex-student in a porn video, he tells me about struggles that happened somewhere in the past. History, sure, I say. I wanna watch buildings explode.

Blowing up buildings, he says, that's nothing, that's nothing new.

Dude, I say, we all know the real war's over images, everyone says that. Nothing important's in buildings anymore powerwise, it's all in computers and shit. I don't wanna blow up buildings cuz I think it'll change the future or the government. I don't wanna achieve some weird utopia. I wanna blow up buildings because the destruction of property excites me sexually.

He considers this. What's your wildest sexual fantasy, he asks. I say: Wildest? Whatever. I say: ruthless gangs of fifteen-year-old boys destroy cities: crumbling archways tumbled statues: stone nipples and calves garnish weedy lots: towering heaps of rubble: buildings explode burn collapse: dilapidated hotels: stairways leading nowhere: packs of dark boys with unruly hair leave me in debris roped ankles handcuffs bandanna gag naked sweating moist asshole quivering waiting: red glow of bonfires pressed against low sky of ash and mist: they come back to me smelling of gunpowder and rage: I like the weight and texture of their bellies on the ascending curve of my buttocks: fuck fuck fuck: they're hot angry and in love: the latino boys call me "gringito": they're real butch.

Later, the old guy tells me I'm too serious and don't know how to have fun. In a few days he falls in love with a different hustler, fresh out of prison.

NOSTALGIA

My first lover was plastic, an eight-inch astronaut I secretly tucked into my underwear at night when I was five: an inert piece of blue matter crawls around my butthole, never enters (my butthole's too small, really, and the astronaut's signaling arms render the project improbable), but suggests the possibility of entering, eroticizing not only the boy's dreams, but outer space and all the distant planets. The one between Pluto and Neptune, for example, where the atmosphere's so heavy the ferns are creepers plus you can mingle with convicts, reptiles, humiliated beings and weird black plants. Later, I'll fall for Chekhov, the handsome Russian helmsman on *Star Trek*, despite the cold war or Captain Kirk's repeated threat to go where no man has gone before. Every day, the boy tightens his sphincter muscles; Captain Kirk is too obvious, idiotic and only supposedly sexy. He's authoritarian and wears his pants dorky. He was born in the same grim town as my father, no lie: Riverside, Iowa, where a replica of the Starship *Enterprise* now squats in the center of town. Pilgrims come from miles away.

Earlier there was Heath on *The Big Valley*, who'll be transformed into the Six Million Dollar Man. The ludicrous sum wasted on his sexy, technologized limbs and bionic power is eerily identical to the number of Jews killed in one of the most recent world wars. The other connection is bad evolutionary mythologies. He won't appeal to the boy either, despite the sexy name: STEVE AUSTIN, implying the sex I'll someday have in small Texas cities (shirtless men walk dark windy highways: against crumbling brick walls that divide nothing from nothing: slide cock in slowly then fuck standing up), only the lost form of Heath hiding somewhere inside the postsurgical body, crackling out in invisible rerun waves, on some lost, distant channel.

IMPERTINENT CASE STUDY:
ATYPICAL PSYCHOSIS & FETISHISM

Smelly women really turn me (Mark) on. My comments about women are often followed by the interjection "phew" used as an exclamation. (Cheryl Ladd, . . . phew! Farrah Fawcett, . . . phew!) I "get sexually excited and experience an urge to masturbate when I hear static from any source," place pictures of women next to a radio and masturbate while it produces static, "experience my most intense arousal during severe thunderstorms." I believe: everyone is excited by static and they use this source of arousal for pleasure and to make others jealous. A farmer's cap pulled down around my eyes, shirt pocket full of pens and pencils, I "not only behave strangely," I look "weird."

"Greatly appreciating the fact that money was the only prerequisite to physical intimacy," I used to have static with prostitutes. Unfortunately, I was discovered masturbating and listening to static by residents at a retirement home where I janitored. I didn't stop; instead I "turned toward the residents and began laughing maniacally." I was "involuntarily committed to an inpatient unit at a local mental health facility."

Doctors fastened a penile strain gauge to measure changes in my penile circumference, one of the most accurate measures of male sexual arousal, and a prelude to a program designed to suppress my deviant outlet for sexual arousal. (Static's a non living, so fetishistic object.) (According to Freud, the penis is the normal prototype of fetishism.) The program was (1) a heterosocial skills training program. (A "person" gains access to normal heterosexual outlets through "a variety of skilled behaviors, such as conversation and dating skills." These skills, collectively called heterosocial skills, must be taught to those who have never learned them.) (2) the "current treatment of choice for eliminating deviant sexual arousal," which "seems to be" aversion therapy, with electric shock used as the aversive stimulus. "Electric shock delivered to the wrist proved to be an effective inhibitor of sexual arousal as measured by penile response." The subject of that last sentence is "electric shock." In any sentence using "shock" or even "aversive stimulus" or "response prevention" you find this passive construction: " shock of ½ second duration was delivered contingent on a 20% full erection response to static . . . ," implying that these shocks are not being delivered by the doctor who wrote the sentences or any other human, but that they emerge spontaneously from the collective unconscious, the late seventies, or perhaps some scary continent like Africa.

"Unfortunately," circumstances beyond my therapist's control brought treatment to a halt. Given a job in a sheltered workshop of tolerant people, I struck up a relationship with a mentally retarded girl who didn't object to the use of static during sex. "Although hardly the basis for an ideal relationship," we talked about marriage. (One of the heterosocial skills I'd been taught.)

CASE STUDY:
POTENTIAL CLIENT ON POLK STREET
I watch bodies that move purposefully, seemingly unaware of their role as sexual objects. A construction worker in pale jeans, shirtless, a Caucasian with tiny dark nipples and a hairless chest. Eighteen, maybe nineteen, in black boots. As he lifts things over his head and armpits, his nipples and flattened stomach become a different sort of zone, temporal as well as

spatial. I imagine the different paths our bodies have taken, through all the usual functions, so we'd both be here in the cold, his body visible to mine. He bends over to pick something up, I shiver. An older man moves next to him, makes him seem harder, stronger, in contrast. Metal scrapes against metal, a crane picks something up, something crumbles. The continual disappearance of unstable images.

It's the potency contained in motion or in rest from motion that I want. A shirtless man leaning against a car alludes to activity, the possibility of robbing banks. Ideally, sex would get lost in the midst of other activity. To fuck, say, between tosses of unwieldy bags of trash onto a garbage truck. The sweaty man heaves, heaves, fucks with the same rhythm and force, thrust, thrust, then back to the job, heave, heave, like that. It's not a need to be considered something trashlike. It's about raising the neglected beauty of garbage to the level of sexual acts. Not worshiping filth like it's some new hallucinated god, but eroticizing everything: even the pointless motion of human labor. Jockstrap, torso, swarthy barbarians. Smelly homeless people splotched with Kaposi's, circling cop cars with AMERIKKKA spray-painted on the sides in shocking pink, roaches swarming over the drying splatter of some despondent queen's vomit on the sidewalk: everything shimmers.

I stare at the Caucasian's nipples. If I stare long enough maybe he'll stare back, a mixture of lust and contempt, swagger over: he would require that I unbutton his trousers. My hand would tremble. The soft penis beneath the blue cloth would not only suggest the idea of night, but merge with it. Sometimes for schizophrenics, and other people too, there isn't any difference between the word and what it represents. The beauty of the penis wouldn't be in the power it symbolized, but in the way it reflected the uselessness of men's nipples, the supple belly leading toward them. It'd be in that space where beauty and terror cross. I don't understand any of that, really, only a vague desire for something solid, someone who'd at least pretend they aren't going to die. Demon lovers. Failing horns I choose petty thieves, felons, tweaks: hustlers and dealers and scamming young boys: pyromaniacs especially: your tongues and nipples and muscular calves, your black baggy trousers and stained fingers, your bulletwounds, tattoos and pathological lying.

My dream date fulfills the criteria for a diagnosis of Antisocial Personality Disorder from the DSM-III. Before the age of 15 he displays 3 or more of such things as: truancy (5 days a year for at least 2 years), suspension from school, delinquency, running away from home overnight at least twice, persistent lying, repeated sexual intercourse in a casual relationship, substance abuse, thefts, vandalism, grades below expectations, chronic violations of rules at home or at school, fighting.

Since the age of 18, at least four of these: inability to sustain consistent work behavior (for example, six months or more of unemployment in five years, when expected to work), lack of ability to function as a responsible parent, failure to respect lawful norms with regard to lawful behavior, inability to maintain enduring attachment to a sexual partner (for example, ten or more sexual partners in a year), irritability and aggressiveness, failure to honor financial obligations, failure to plan ahead or impulsivity, disregard for the truth, recklessness.

My dream date resembles Brad Davis in Fassbinder's *Querelle* more than the pathetic trade on Polk. Like psychologists I generalize and stylize lawbreakers. They attempt to identify and correct, I romanticize and adore. When I get robbed and punched in the face I just feel stupid and sick. Later, the episode enters my fantasy life and becomes something unbearably sexy.

CASE STUDY:
HUSTLERS

We had spray-painted the word RUINS on various walls in various cities, as well as the word CIVILIZATION, generally used as the object of a rather forceful verb. We know then, from experience, that RUINS is a more attractive word than CIVILIZATION and easier to spell in a hurry. These facts alone seem to explain the general tendencies of things, tendencies we like to encourage, out of boredom, nausea, and a rage so intense sometimes that we can't think of anything much to do.

Cars circle us. A man picks us up, says: I'm not a cop, are you a cop? We say: I'm not a cop. He drives us around, says lately he's been feeling like a serial killer. This is one of those times we should just get out of the car. Still, he doesn't look like a serial killer, despite what they say about the pressures building on the boy next door. Would a serial killer say that he felt like one? Seems they'd probably feel like something else, or at least explain their feelings with different terms than normal guys. We're not too sure about that one. Anyway, he lets us out; not big enough, genitally speaking.

A DISEMBODIED VOICE

It isn't just the body of a boy that we desire. It's the universe that includes them, vectors of pool balls, fluids in glasses, warmth of the bar next to cold of the street, variance in temperatures, colors, flows excite us as much as bodies of boys which move and are moved by all sorts of visible or metabolic forces. Props and buildings put words in our mouths, chemicals in our cells: drab storefronts, darkened doorways, neon signs, circling cars. A mall must exist before it occurs to us to exercise inside it. This could be interpreted as yet one more rationale for pointless terrorist actions against industrial parks, high-rent housing, telecommunication hubs, B. Dalton: rites performed ecstatically, without resentment and without getting caught. Arson: a reminder to the universe of its true nature, for me a message of love. The arsonists themselves, I consider anonymous lovers. Safer sex for the new world order.

VOICE IN A BODY

Jim kept saying: I'm gonna fuck you, never had a hard-on. Kept trying to stick an unlubed finger up my ass. Stop it. *Stop it*. He lived alone, liked to watch men play pool: arrogant hets embarrassed by aging transvestites. Beauty of broken symmetries and porcelain balls. A porcelain ball is ideal for shattering car windows: how those windows crack in crystalline patterns and then just empty with a tap. A few clinging shards around the edges. The bar is REFLECTIONS. Jim paid sixty while we were still in the cab, but wanted that I stay all night. The crystalline is an expression of certain atomic or molecular characteristics at a macroscopic level. First sign of daylight I took off, light cracking the cloudy sky, hilltop view of the city, then rode the bus down Market Street and home.

This guy in the bar says: you don't look like a hustler, you look erudite. Says: You know what the word erudite means? Nope, I say. Then you aren't, he says. Wants me to spend the whole night in Marin for twenty bucks. Dude, I say, take a hike.

Go to the hot tubs with a john from Mountain View, a racist Buddhist Caucasian. You don't say much, he says. Tells me how sweet I am, how gentle. While I'm massaging his neck I'm imagining breaking it. Crack, the shattered bones like glass.

Some guy says there's no such thing as safe sex with a hustler. You can't even masturbate because you might infect yourself. When you imagine your own dissolution it isn't so much at the level of the body's decay, it's atoms splitting down, electrons spinning off into nothing, matter and antimatter obliterating each other, reclaiming the flickering void. On *Star Trek* once Captain Kirk met his evil antimatter twin and triumphed over him in an ugly dualistic parable, aided by his cronies: the pointy-eared logician and the doctor. Meanwhile, the real news: Chekhov shimmered paleolithically, a palpable blue erotic light pulsing electric from his mouth, his anus, his slowly disappearing form.

We can sense the radiation from post-cold war nuclear tests spreading toward us, across the deserts and brown dead California mountains. We are dizzy with a strange nausea: we want to vomit up the globe. We are spoiled little children, how can this be, that we are going to die?

I don't feel too good anymore, I feel kind of bad.

This guy tells me about a fifteen-year-old boy he knew from the Larkin Street Youth Center who got picked up hustling and murdered. This guy says to me: oh, sure, white boy, you're so hip on burning down buildings, maybe I'll come into your neighborhood, maybe I'll burn down your building, see how you like that. Dude, I say. His Caucasian face is red and puffy. I turn my back on him, calmly walk away.

CASE STUDY:
EROTICO-APOCALYPTIC REVERIE
At the request of an eerie, yet sexy voice on TV, young people slit their parents' throats, run out into the hot vibrating suburban streets to burn down housing subdivisions and retail furniture outlets and Denny's

etc. Baroque cathedrals, skyscrapers, condominiums, The Gap, shopping malls and museums burst into fragments. Family values explode and our elected leaders hang from trees under pale moons, blown about by the wind. Ash drifts through the sky. A handsome boy with baggy trousers and hands blackened by the flesh of noblemen he's been burning screws me for an hour in every position he can think of, often standing. Hands on my thin waist. Lifts me like I'm no heavier than a jumble of bones, a crisscross of smoke and sunlight, a small hungry animal. Nestles me into empty curved spaces of his body, tests my lips and asshole with dextrous fingers, fucks me gently as I hang there in air, my body now a body and tingling all over. Meanwhile, the globe explodes in pretty colorful patterns, naked boys dance around bonfires, and vampire cows, the results of genetic experiments gone awry, pop out of a hazed background of feedback and squealing grungy guitars to soar through a purplish lightning-streaked sky. And so forth. We want death to include cool visuals, a sense of community, some sort of meaning, erotic ecstatic transcendence as opposed to (e) none of the above. We demand the collapse of Western civilization we've been promised since we were children. Maybe there's really more than the two choices of annihilation or scribbling ever more intricate graffiti on prison walls, but we're bored. (In linguistic structures it's the sentence that represents our free will: with a limited number of words we, humans, can produce an infinite number of sentences, such as these: At this point in history, mass destruction is the only thing which is sufficiently entertaining. Please, everything burst.)

BACK ON POLK STREET

This guy wants to give me money, then hurt me. He's kind of smart and likable and he's got the same name as me, even spells it with a PH. He tweaks my nipples. He likes my eye contact as he fishes around inside me. Like prisons, schools and twelve-step recovery programs, he wants a docile body to subject, use, transform and arrange in space. He says he has a piece of my shit lodged between his fingers and that's never happened before. I'm not enjoying this, I say. No, he says, but you take it real good.

84

I've heard that at a certain point of pain my soul'll snap right out of my body and watch it all from above, but I guess we're nowhere near that place. His fantasies depend on how much control he feels in his own life: if things are going well he just wants to kiss and be held. At the other extreme he wants a seven-year-old boy bound with so much rope that only his mouth and his asshole are showing. We're somewhere in between.

New Year's Eve in the bar a guy says: I bet you'll never guess what I'm into. I suggest he simply tell me. Light S&M, he says. No, really? He wants me to be a master. I've never done it, I say, but I think I can use my imagination. Back at his apartment I bind his ankles with neckties. When I spit in his mouth he wishes I'd been drinking beer all night. I say DOWN ON YOUR KNEES YOU SCUMBAG PIECE OF

SHIT. I say KISS MY NIPPLES LICK MY ARMPIT
LICK MY TATTOO YOU FUCKING SCUMBAG
PIECE OF SHIT. While he goes at my underarm his
head's cradled in my arm and I say: I could crush you,
YOU ARE NOTHING YOU'RE A WORTHLESS
PIECE OF SLIMY SHIT I DON'T KNOW IF
YOU'RE DOGSHIT OR CATSHIT OR LIZARD-
SHIT BUT YOU SURE AS HELL AIN'T NO
HUMANSHIT. He says, are you sure you've never
done this before? I say, I WAS BORN TO BE A
MASTER, SCUMBAG and I think it might be true:
we could take matter into our own hands, we could
form it, burn it, fill the world with beautiful things.
On the other hand, we might die trying. On the other
hand, we might die regardless. Towering over a fragile
body it's hard to imagine that someday it'll be like I
was never here at all: vanished, with everything else,
and you: we finish, wipe off the bodily fluids, zip
up, and go out together into the night: it's New Year's
Eve and the night is so excellent: bound to disappoint,
but still: we can go anywhere in it, anywhere at all.

THAT'S WHAT FRIENDS ARE FOR

Neil Bartlett

My Father said to me, he said, son, don't you ever worry about growing old?

He said, don't *you* ever worry about growing old?

And I said, well father what really worries me is whether I'll get the chance to grow old, I mean sometimes I wonder whether they're going to let us. . . .

But if I do, if I do grow old, then it's going to be just fine, it's going to be just fine, because I've got so many friends.

I've got so many friends.

I've got one to love me,
One to make love to me,
I've got one to lend me clothes, I've got one to take me dancing,
I've got four to keep me warm at night,

I've got seven to pick me up when I'm down,
I've got seven to pick me up anyway,
I've got—

He said, but don't you ever get scared?

I said well when I get scared then I just call up one of my friends.
He said, won't you be lonely?
I said, when I get lonely, I just call up my friends.
He said, but who's going to cook your dinner?
I said, I'll cook the dinner, I'll invite some friends round; and you can bring the wine.

He said, who's going to take you to the hospital.
I said, well, I'll just call up one of my friends.
He said:
You don't have a wife, you won't have any children, you don't even drive a car—
And I said it's going to be alright.
It is going to be alright,
Because I've got so many friends. . . .

And I called up my first friend and he said I'll be right over and I opened the door and he held out his hand and he took me in his arms and he held me tight and he held on to me, he held me together, he held me down, he laid me down and he made love to me all . . . night . . . long.

And then I called up my second friend and he said, hello? and I said, I'm sorry. I really don't know why I'm calling you, it's three o'clock in the morning, and he said, it's OK I was up anyway, I said yes but I don't know why I'm calling you, he said: it's OK, I can't sleep either, I don't know anyone who can these days.

And then I called up my third friend well he's not a friend really I just met him down the pub, it's the same every weekend I say don't do this to yourself, don't do it, but you know, what can you do, there you are, three o'clock in the morning and you're walking home together of course we couldn't get a taxi, three o'clock, there she is, walking down the middle of the bloody road, singing her head off, and I said, what is she like?

She's like a child, she's like my sister; she's like a mother to me that one, she's my best girl friend.

And I called up my fourth friend but he wasn't there so I called up my fifth friend and I said I'm so sad, he said it would be better to be angry, and I said I'm so sad, he said it would be better to be angry, I said: but I'm so sad. He said, you might feel better if you practiced getting angry.

I called up my sixth friend and he said look I've got no more advice to give you but I can give you this if you think it will make you feel better and he gave me a big bottle of red wine and on the label he had written I KNOW JUST HOW YOU FEEL and that's what you need sometimes, someone who knows just exactly what it feels like. . . .

So I called up my seventh friend

And my seventh friend lent me his books he lent me
his records, he cooked me dinner, he drove me home
and he put me to bed, he listened to my story, he
heard me out, he talked me out of it, he disagreed
with me;
He knew what he was saying;
He knew what he was talking about;
He made five practical suggestions about how I might
improve my situation

My eighth friend checks me for bruises, he calls me
back to make sure I'm alright and he lets me cry for
as long as I want to and when we're walking down
the street he never lets go of my hand, not ever.

And my ninth friend said do you know, I haven't had
this much fun in three years. . . .

and my tenth friend said Darling, I think I'm going
to like you with white hair. . . .

and my Father said, but who's going to come to your
funeral

. . . . and I said

. . . . well I said

. . . . That's What Friends Are For.

WHERE IS LOVE?

Neil Bartlett

YOU CAN HEAR the sweet boy treble of Mark Lester from the original recording of Lionel Bart's *Oliver!* singing "Where Is Love?" As the song begins to imperceptibly fade, a spotlight reveals a microphone. At the microphone, a man. He is wearing boots, jeans, a black leather jacket with nothing under it. Black leather gloves, greased hair, a Marlboro and a can. He begins to talk but you can't quite hear what he is saying because of the music and because he is talking so gently and quietly. He is very still and quiet. Later on he takes off his jacket and raises his voice. What he is saying is:

Can you hear me? Can you hear me? Can you hear me now? What have I got to do to make you hear me. What have I got to do to be heard. What have I got to do to make you listen to me, because it always seems there ain't no charity these days. Can you hear me now? That's good, because I want you to hear what I'm saying. I want you to understand what I'm saying. I want to talk to you. I want to talk to you . . . but if you like, I could send you a letter. I could type it. I could send you a report, I could get them to type it— we have all the statistics right here. I could show you some photos, that way you'll know what it looks like. I could introduce you to some friends of mine, to some people I know. Or if you like, we could just meet, you and me. I could come to your office, or if you'd like, you could come to my place. Or we could just talk on the phone. Would it be better for you if I talked very quietly? Or would you hear me better if I talked very loud. I could practice getting angry if you liked. Would it be better if I practiced getting angry or if I practiced not getting angry? Can you hear me now? How many of us do there have to be before you can hear me? Are there enough of us yet?

Are there enough of us here? Are there enough people in this office? Do we have enough volunteers? Do we have enough people to man the phones? Could you get us another phone put in? Do we have enough people for the phones, enough people for the T-shirts, enough for the buckets, enough to count the money? If you like, I could fix it so that there are fifteen thousand of us. Because you see I think it's very important that people should get involved. I think everyone should get involved in this kind of effort. And as my own personal contribution to tonight's effort I should like to sing you all a little song. I should like to raise your consciousness. I should like to raise some cash. I should like to raise the roof. And I should like to dedicate this song to everyone here tonight, to all of you and to all of us who are HIV-positive. And I would like to dedicate this song to all of us and to all of you who have attended funerals in the past twelve months, and to all of us who won't be here next year, and I would like to dedicate this song to all my friends and to my dear friends and to my colleagues and to my lovers and most especially I would like to dedicate this song to Trevor and to Gene and to Ethyl and to Mark and to Steve. And I would like to dedicate this song to everyone here tonight who has been to bed with me. And I would like to dedicate this song to everyone here tonight who would like to go to bed with me. Anyone here who would like to take me home. It's OK, I'm staying with friends, but we could just make less noise than usual, they wouldn't mind. And I would like to dedicate this song to everyone here tonight who'd like to fuck me. Everyone here who'd like to have safe sex with me. Everyone here who would like to have unsafe sex with me. I mean, we're not actually going to do it but that doesn't mean we're not going to think about it. And I'd like to dedicate this song to anybody here tonight who'd like to tie me up. Anyone here tonight who'd like to get real dirty with me, anyone who'd like to tell me all about it, anyone who thinks well they've never been into that kind of thing but maybe with me they could be. I'd like to dedicate this song to anybody who fancies me just because I'm dressed like this, and I would like to dedicate this song to all those people who have in the last three months verbally or physically abused, assaulted or humiliated me because I am a homosexual, and I would most especially like to dedicate this song to the six men I met on the number

fifteen bus last Wednesday evening and I would like
to say boys this one is for you, boys I would like to
give you . . . I would like to give you a piece of my
mind

I would like to give you
a helping hand

I would like to give you
a shot in the arm
a shoulder to cry on

I would like to give you
all of me.

Why not?
Take all of me. Can't you see, I'm no good without
     you?
Take these lips; I'll never use them.
Take these arms; I want to lose them.
Your goodbyes left me with eyes that cry
How can I go on dear without you;
You took the part that once was my heart,
So come on,
Take all of me.
All of me—why not? Take all of me. . . .
You took the Best.
So come on;
Take the rest
Oh
Baby
Take all of me.

SHE SAID LOSS, LOST

Akilah Nayo Oliver

tina turner on acid yodeling in arabic. however goes
the night. yersterday rocks touched my feet. asked
if i remembered promise how it felt cutting your wet
jeans in the pigeon stained sand & how the pigeons
masqueraded as seagulls. i haven't seen them for a
long time. lots of things gone. bell on an ice cream
truck. my favorite line already happened. on the radio
a voice sounds like a teasing three year old & the horn
section goes nanananana.
all the knowing. the closed fisted salutes. how come
nobody mentioned clitorectomy with they dashikis on.
like we were afraid a close look. a criticism. a
rejection of a fixed ritual would pop the bubble.
dreams are fragile like that. they conceal as much
as they reveal. the colors proscribed in song. imagining
the world as placed. fixed.

you a visitor in a land scape you don't control
i want to know what the

eyes smelled at the bottom of the ships. i've seen

that look of terror before. any asshole on the bus
pants hanging off his butt. X terrorizing a fashion
statement on hats & t-shirts. any black boy beautiful
   or ugly
could be of my blood. one meaning of blackness.
this arbitrariness of circumstance.

knowing its all possible & nothing's true.

where's the national
museum with the slave ships. whips. neck silencers.
   irons.
chains. mouth bits. if i said the ships. why wouldn't
we all immediately have a common reference. where
is the national tongue. the informed language for
this thing called slavery. i don't know of anyone
who knows the names of their great great great great
grandfathers. not the mythic ones or adopted ones.
the exact people who birthed you. i don't know of
anyone who knows the faces of their grandmothers'
rapists. not any face. the face. i don't know anyone
who can sing an old freedom song. where are the
stories of the torture. what did women do with their
   hair.
where are the seers. what the hell does raw cotton
feel like. bales & bales & generations of it.

SEND OUT THE SONG SINGERS FOR ME, O LORD

Akilah Nayo Oliver

1.
my blood runs wild in the night air & i am starved
i scratched on the walls till dawn & the bastards
they heard all the other sirens i know
they heard me too
/send out the song singers for me o lord i'm gonna
    move on/
it's almost like there is no context for your body
the way you float one of those escaped angels
lighting the twisted boulevard hunched like old men

2.
oh what to do with a swollen body that aches to be
eaten like swollen strawberries that know
they'll only be alive for a time

3.
who sees the sweet goddess in me
the night walking on candlestick legs

4.
i resist the slow stampede into the church doors
they say a welcome blotted in stained glass &
plain boards stuck in a cross on western
avenue & 38th street
i want this savior to come out
i want to see him naked in daylight
i want to see him change into many women
who like surprise change into thousands of sensations
right before my eyes
i want to see him erect under an eye
that does not look away

5.
nothing seems to dismiss
the particulars of this tragedy
to the degree that loneliness is a tragedy
when politicized
a shared depression

6.
i would not have thought i would be so common
had you asked me ten or even twelve years ago
my name
i would have given an answer
encased in flaming *geles* piled
high on heads like proud water buckets
perfectly balanced
i would not have known what you meant
had you said: it is not the loneliness
                that will eat you alive

  but the sentencing to this exile
  as the city tortures with oblivious
   movement
  crashing through the silence
  a kind of teasing
  a wiff of clove dancing by

7.
there are other crimes & the calling of this
blasphemous is debatable:
  this god in those doors exists
  because we will him breathe
  not the spirit of him
  but the physicality of him
  he is male & omnipotent   99
  we make him caress our wounds
  our fat black mother failed wounds
  he touches with the steady hands
  of the lover who inflicted them
  he breaks our idea of sexual pleasure
  he holds a stern finger to our clits
  & when we are finally melted
  & able to do no more dreaming
  he orders us to crawl on our tongues
  to his bloodied feet
  & we are to do it
  in an unacknowledged orgasm
  & then we are saved

WHY I WRITE

Akilah Nayo Oliver

for all those times we leapt into clear morning unable
to state our given names,

for the dachau trees & middle passage limbs when we
argued whose pain was more worthy of attention,

for the loose teeth of a vegetarian father who could
not look death in the eye to feel exonerated,

for the faceless woman who said, how do i know the
bitch is my mother, i only met her when i was fifteen,

for the dead brother who sat on brick wall with me
as we plotted to run away together to the revolution,

for the priviledge of forgetting as we walk down the
dingy abandoned streets intellectualizing our
      advances,

for the masturbatory devices stuck in my pussy while
a voice that lives inside me moaned bitch, bitch,
      sweet bitch,

for the pathetic mother at busstop who looked at me

wit my son urging me to protect as she waited for
the 38 bus to ride her to the county jail to visit hers,

for the gold capped tooth laugh of the angry queen
who walks the street behind her grocery cart speaking
    sphinx,

for the sad language scrawled on walls articulating
a despair only the initiated can decipher,

for the dream of white horses & white knights &
    white
powder & virtual reality,

for the ungood & the unforgiving bullets that clip
the silence & punctuate the ends of my sentences,

for the time i left you spinning in circles in a loveless
rain wondering where home was,

for the brooklyn snow molded into the concrete
    cracks
that accepted my impression passionately as seasoned
    whores,

for the seasoned 'ho in me,

for the time i touched your fat shoulder with my
    finger
tip & felt you give up the ghost of the martyred
    mother,

for the need to submit to something both lower &
    higher than
myself,

for the common emancipation of language unleashed,

for the knock kneed little skinny girlchild who
    learned her name
was mine.

MORPHIA

Patrick McGrath

I WAS WALKING with your mother down a dark deserted street of decaying Georgian houses behind the hospital. It was a cool evening. The sky was not black, rather that curious shade of dark blue that makes you think of the hour before dawn. Strips of cloud scudded across a gibbous moon like rags and streamers chasing some ghostly night parade. Your mother had linked her arm in mine, and drawn in close to me, pressing against me as we walked. I'd told her about Henry Vaughan, who lay unconscious in the hospital in Griffin Head, and just talking about my fear that I'd caused his illness made it seem absurd. "Probably an aneurysm," said your mother. "It was there in his brain long before you even met me."

She was not angry that I'd broken my promise and telephoned her. She told me she liked it that I needed her. Ratcliff never needed her, she said, he was self-sufficient, always in control. He had never shown weakness. Why should this make her unhappy? It stifled her. His strength stifled and limited her, such that she felt needed only by her child, by you, and even you were slipping away from her now, slipping into manhood and all that went with it.

How sad she was that night, almost as if she knew what was about to happen, all the horror. I hadn't dared to ask her if she'd changed her mind, so I didn't know if we were going on as before, or if these were our last moments. We stopped beneath a lamppost. Cupping her cheeks in my hands, my fingers still smelling of antiseptic, I kissed her eyes and forehead and the tip of her nose and felt again the familiar, potent, unsteady wave come coursing through me and leave me trembling, for it was at times too much, what I felt for her. The streetlight bathed her features in a yellowy radiance, her parted lips, her eyes searching my face, the frown of anxiety and unhappiness. "Darling Edward," she murmured. We walked on. The scene is etched in my mind.

When she let herself back into the house the light in the study was on and the door was open. "Is that you?" Ratcliff called, and she paused in the doorway of the study. "How is Brenda?"

"Brenda's fine."

"And Anthony?"

"I didn't see Anthony."

"Like to sit down and have a drink?"

"I think I won't, Ratcliff. I'm going up."

"As you please."

Anger then, surely, a black surge of it that he must have controlled only with the utmost difficulty. She wouldn't even sit down and have a drink with him. But he did control it. He had determined the course of action he would follow, and he was not going to sabotage it with rash outbursts, no matter what the provocation.

At this point, of the three of us, only Ratcliff fully understood what we were moving toward, only he knew that these in a sense were the last days. Your mother must have suspected, but we'd parted on a somewhat ambivalent note. As for me, what was about to happen, what Ratcliff was about to do, would come as the most violent of shocks, and have the most far-reaching of consequences—I feel them to this day.

Oh God.

So was this why you abandoned me, was this why you renounced me, threw me over, left me broken, in *all* senses broken—shunned, ignored, wretched, friendless, alone? Surely not, surely you would not so easily surrender what we had, yet you did, you allowed him to drive a wedge between us—!

Oh God.

He called you into the study again, didn't he? Isn't that how it happened? He called you in—you didn't want to see him then, he'd already hinted to you that he'd found out, and I imagine Brenda had telephoned by this time and told you about his calling her—so you must have known what was up. He was standing by the fireplace. "What is it, Ratcliff?" you said, and you avoided his eye as you crossed the room to the cigarette case on the low table, and busied yourself there. You were in gray that evening, the gray dress of soft wool, long-sleeved and tightly belted at the waist, which I loved—you moved across the room in that clingy dress, that sheath of gray wool, and stood frowning as you lit your cigarette and Ratcliff started in on you. *Why* did you give in to him? Oh, he is a man of strong will, I know, I've experienced the force of his personality, I've seen him storming down the

corridors of St. Basil's so I do understand how intimidating he can be. But you are strong also! And didn't you think of me—that I was *with* you, and could give you all the support you might possibly need? All you had to do was stand firm in front of him for those few minutes, defy the man, refuse to crumble before his inquisition—why, why, my darling, need that have been so difficult, when you *knew* I was waiting, and you *knew* the strength of my commitment—? But you did. You allowed him to overwhelm you, and though I have been shattered and destroyed by this I bear no anger toward you. You were not strong enough—I understand. He told you he knew you weren't at Brenda's; he was bluffing, but you weren't to know this.

Oh God—

Oh God, not you, darling boy, your *mother*! Your *mother*! Oh my angel, my precious boy—

I have a picture in my mind of your mother coming into your bedroom, late at night, and you sitting at your table with a lamp focused on the model aeroplane you're building, and her standing there in the doorway, smoking, her dark form framed by the light from the upstairs landing, watching, silently, as with slim precise fingers you delicately assemble a wing—

Flight—how you loved flight—

And do you remember the evenings we had in Elgin? When we talked of ideas like the spirit, and the higher will, and service? And the quest for the infinite? You'd come after evening surgery, perhaps share the cold supper Mrs. Gregor had left, then we'd go upstairs. I'd read to you in the study, or we'd simply talk. Often we wouldn't turn the lights on, we'd watch the sunset smoldering on the horizon, burnishing the lip of the sea. I'd offer you a drink, but generally you refused. Oh, there was something in the atmosphere of that large, empty house, with the last glow of sunset, the gloom, the poetry we'd shared—a coming together of influences that was intoxicating for both of us, do you remember? I once told you facetiously after we'd read a little Swinburne together that we were bound to win the war because we were so much crueler than the Germans, and when (a little bewildered I suspect!) you asked me why I thought so, I clapped shut the Swinburne, waved it in the air, and cried: "That's why!" That made you laugh, didn't it!

Oh, and I'd pace the room, I'd limp up and down, talking of this and that—in a certain sort of mood, with a certain sort of listener, and among my own books, I'm the kind of man who can talk for hours on end without once repeating himself, or failing to entertain, and you of course know how to listen, I always appreciated that in you, and listen you did, you gave me the sympathetic ear I needed, you encouraged me to wander, intellectually, from topic to topic, and occasionally, inevitably, I'd drift into areas of purely personal concern. I remember once showing you a picture I was particularly fond of, a reproduction of a romantic painting of a heap of icy debris in an empty polar vastness, and telling you that landscape was a state of the soul; and when you looked doubtful I said painting should never be an act of imitation but rather a refusal to imitate, because art, after all, must finally aspire to passion—and you said, "Passion?"

I paused in my pacing, I limped to the window and gazed out. "She believed it was the best we were capable of," I murmured, "civilized human beings."

"Who did?"

This was asked in the softest of tones, it was the merest breath from the shadows. I said nothing. I leaned my forearm on the window sash, then leaned my forehead against my arm, and allowed my weight to rest on my good leg as I looked out at the sea, from which the last of the sunset had by this time vanished entirely. Neither of us broke the silence. You knew who I was talking about. I said this. You said, "She thought there was nothing better than passion? Physical passion?"

The moral asceticism of youth. "I don't think it was quite as simple as that," I said, turning from the window and facing you across the darkness. "I don't think you should judge her harshly."

"She never wanted me to fly," you said. You were all in shadow at the far end of the room, in an old high-backed wing chair of Peter Martin's. "She tried to convince me there wouldn't be a war."

"She loved you," I said. "She wanted to protect you. It's a mother's natural instinct."

"I asked her if she was against fascism. She said of course she was, but she was against war too."

"And?"

"I said she couldn't be against both of them."

It suddenly came to me, and with devastating clarity, that I was losing you. That after tonight you would never come back. You'd reached some sort of decision about your mother and the part I'd played in her life, and there was no more you wanted to know, even though I had barely begun the task of explaining it to you. "I don't think she really understood what was at stake," you said, and for the first time I heard in your voice, and in your thinking, the unmistakable tone of Ratcliff, and my heart sank. The idea that you would carry with you, perhaps for the rest of your life, Ratcliff's idea of her, and his contemptuous dismissal of our love affair and all that it meant—it was unthinkable. I flailed about in my mind for some means, any means, to prevent this happening. "Did your father talk to you about her illness?" I said.

I saw you turn toward me in the gloom. A pause.

"Why do you ask?"

"I wish I could have seen her, that's all."

"But why?"

I gave a slight shrug and turned back toward the window—oh, I had promised myself never to bring this up with you, but I was desperate, desperate not to lose you! "It's nothing," I murmured. "These cases—these obscure kidney conditions—they're complicated. Tricky to diagnose properly."

Again a pause. "You think she was diagnosed wrongly?"

"No no no. No, I'm sure everything was done that could be done. I'd have liked to examine her myself, that's all."

What did you make of this? I couldn't tell; you were of course far too delicate to impute to me a dishonorable motive. Silently the moments passed, and I hated myself for what I was doing—sowing a seed of unease, this was what I was doing, planting suspicion in you, suspicion that would only fester until it brought you to me again.

You rose to leave soon afterwards, troubled, I could see, by our conversation but unsure just why. I shook your hand at the front door, and you were always so sweet when you left me, rather formal, rather apologetic for having taken so much of my time. As if I had anything better to do! You mounted your bicycle, and I watched you wobble off down the drive in the dusk, wheels crunching on the gravel, small and slim and upright in the saddle. Just where the drive turns out onto the coast road you turned to wave and you saw me there in my black corduroy jacket and snowy white shirt, a silk cravat at my throat, and I lifted a hand, standing in the doorway of my dark, soaring, narrow house, then turned and went inside and closed the front door behind me, and so into the surgery to see to Spike. All this, of course, before our relationship became one of doctor and patient.

Doctor and patient ... I am aware, at times, of the grandeur of my spirit. At such times I find it absurd that it is housed in this puny frame, which has become, since Spike, a ruin. This is why I fell in love with Elgin, it offered a structure adequate to me, for I am not a small man *spiritually*. It is a jest of nature and an irony of circumstance that I am trapped in this flawed and puny frame, though never, I think, has it been brought home to me so clearly, until I met you, or rather, until you began to suffer your peculiar glandular disturbance, just how far this tendency in nature for botch and error can go. For my concern that you understand the nature of my relationship with your mother was soon to be overshadowed by my concern for *you*, for you and what started happening to you as you continued daily to face violent death.

My last real encounter with your father occurred as I emerged, one afternoon, into the hospital lobby from the basement stairs, hard by the bench where your mother and I had made love. He was in a dark green leather apron under his white coat, about to descend. He stopped dead and glared at me. I believe the sight of me enraged him. I believe he had worked himself into such a state of jealous rage he was unable to control himself. He seized me by the arm. He called me an odious worm. He said I was furtive, insidious and contemptible. He said I couldn't begin to understand the mischief I was creating, the harm I was doing: all this he hissed at me in a low voice that attracted no one's attention, a cigar between his teeth, all the while gripping my upper arm so hard I couldn't get away from him. It was when he accused me of harming your mother that I made my retort, and given what I've told you, you will understand that I acted with restraint, much good it did me. All I said was, words to the effect that it was *he* who'd harmed her, and that he wasn't worthy of her. He fell silent. He let go of my arm and turned away, then suddenly turned back and with a sort of vicious swatting motion he slapped me with the back of his hand, very hard. The speed of the attack took me completely by surprise. I am a small man, and it knocked me off balance. My spectacles flew off. I remember thinking, in that first fraction of an instant when the mind operates with a sort of mad clarity, that I could regain my balance by flailing my arms about. So with white coat flapping, and stethoscope leaping wildly off my chest, and canting steeply backward, I windmilled there at the top of the stairs, but to no avail. I fell badly and hit the landing halfway down.

Of the fall itself I have no memory. One moment I

stood flailing at the top of the staircase, the next I was lying in a heap on the landing, and when I tried to move there flared in my hip pain such as I had never before experienced, and would never have thought possible. Even as I lay there, nauseous, unwilling to attempt the smallest movement lest it bring back the pain, I was perfectly aware of what had happened, I had a clear picture of the pathology, it was quite obvious, really, after a fall like that: the neck of the femur was fractured. I'd broken my hip.

I suppose I must have passed out then. A dim awareness of faces and voices, of being loaded onto a stretcher, carried upstairs, and everything that jarred the hip had me crying out with pain. It wasn't until I was on a bed that someone gave me a shot of morphia and then, mercifully—nothing. The last thought I had, as the needle went in, was the phrase "pin and traction."

A broken hip is pretty straightforward. You open it up, dissect away the muscle, and bang in a steel pin. It's called a Smith-Petersen, and it holds the broken ends together. During cold weather, or when I'm tired, or if I've been on my feet too long, it'll produce inflammation in the femuro-pelvic joint, where the neck of the thighbone fits into the pelvis. Then it hurts like the devil, and that's when I need a shot of morphia to keep me cheerful—you know how I am when Spike's not behaving. And if it hadn't been for your father knocking me down the stairs that day

I'd never have known the pleasure of Spike's company.

The ironies began crowding in on me thick and fast now. Not least among them was being admitted to St. Basil's as a patient, and then being assigned to a bed on my own surgical ward, with McGuinness my attending physician. It was a Nightingale ward, fifteen beds down either side of a long, high-ceilinged room, each with the patient's fever chart attached to a clipboard and dangling from a hook at the foot of the bed. The floors were parquet, and squeaked, the walls were painted pale green to shoulder height, white above, and there were three large windows down each wall with potted plants on the sills. The smell of antiseptic permeated everything. It was a busy place, patients shuffling about in dressing gowns, being wheeled off for this test or that—nurses running up and down—ward rounds morning and evening, when McGuinness would move from bed to bed with Sister—and twice a week grand rounds with Cushing himself.

God how I came to dread the sound of his footsteps as he came clattering upstairs from the senior common room! I'm well aware of the attitude surgeons hold toward fracture patients, they're a nuisance, frankly, tedious and time-consuming and not very interesting. They need X rays, cast changes, adjustments in traction, there are always a thousand small things to be done for them, and you can never relax, for although pinning a hip is the most common procedure on fracture service, once you've started the operation the chances of infection increase in almost direct proportion to the length of time the incision is open. The body will tolerate the pin only as long as there's no infection around it, so if infection does set in it can't be cleared until the pin is removed, and then you have to start all over again. So you must get it right first time and pretty quickly too. Cushing took a sort of grim relish in pointing all this out to me.

But the dominant feature of the period immediately after your father attacked me was the pain. Cushing operated the next day, whistling Puccini throughout, I'm told, and then I was put in traction, my leg suspended from the knee with weights attached to the ankle to stop the muscles pulling the pin out of alignment. The pain began with each return to consciousness, built rapidly to a peak, where it held with such excruciating intensity it had me twisting from side to side doing everything I could to keep from screaming, and not always succeeding. McGuinness would be sent for (it all seemed to take forever), but when he finally appeared, and made his way down the ward to me, rather than feel relief at his approach I would grow ever more frantic and by the time he reached my bed I'd literally be *begging* for the needle, and not even the twitch of contempt in his face could silence me, that's how bad it was.

Oh, never presume to judge the severity of another's pain! Never presume to judge what can be borne— dear boy, I need hardly tell *you* this. McGuinness would sit at my bedside, frowning, as he drew the fluid into the barrel of the syringe, and he'd murmur:

"Calm down, man, you'll get your shot"—and even in my bleary wretchedness I could read his mind, he was thinking it contemptible that a man (and a doctor) should humiliate himself like this on a public ward. I didn't care. I just wanted the needle. At last I'd feel the prick, then the prickle, then I'd begin to sweat, my mouth would go dry, the pain would ease, and I'd lie there, soaked in sweat, gazing up at the Balkan frame of steel bars and pulleys over the bed, and in the now misty remnants of consciousness I'd breathe a prayer of thanks. Soon I'd drift into a shallow, restless sleep.

I gaze out over the airfield now and try to shake off the shame that clings to the memory of those days. It was terrible, terrible—the indignity of being dependent on the nurses for bowel and bladder functions. Being unable to turn over in bed, or reach for a book or a cigarette. Crumbs getting into the sheets. But worst of all, the pain. I tried to keep the injections down to two a day but I always needed more. I tried to control it—I bore it as best I could—but when it began truly to bite, when it climbed to that crest and simply *did not break*—then I'd feel my willpower loosen and shred like the fiber of an old rubber band. McGuinness would come, eventually, his face a mask of professional neutrality but I could see the pity and scorn it concealed. With wordless efficiency he'd give me my shot and after a moment or two the pain ebbed away, the lights grew brighter and I'd start to feel better, though curiously it wasn't that it disappeared, it was still there but it had lost the power to dominate consciousness to the exclusion of all else, it didn't matter, somehow, it didn't *hurt* anymore.

I'd know then a sense of expanding wonder; voices on the ward seemed to come from a thousand miles away, I'd think of your mother, and my heart would grow tender. Even then, you see, even in that utter extremity of suffering, she was with me, she was my inspiration, and I have come to believe that without her—without the knowledge that she was in the world, loving me—which I took on faith, she never visited me of course—without that, those early days would have been impossible. For I believe (Peter Martin taught me this) that spirit can be mobilized to a thera-peutic end. My will to heal, to create a bony union in my femur, was in those first days grounded in the idea of your mother, so in a very real sense it was *through her* that I was able to inspire the resources of my body to fuse the fragments into a whole.

But they were strange and terrible, those days and nights in traction. I once awoke in darkness to the certainty that the wires of my Balkan frame were the spars and rigging of a ship, an eerie death ship about to cast off and carry me over a subterranean sea to some island of the dead from which I would never return. I struggled to get off the ship and in my panic managed to set the whole frame shaking, the whole complicated system of weights and pulleys, and in the process damn nearly tore Spike clean out of my hip. The night sister later told me that it was only with the greatest difficulty that they were able to subdue me and settle me down with a needle, for in my efforts to get off the ship I'd somehow found the strength of ten men.

When finally I was allowed out of bed, and started hobbling up and down the ward on crutches, I was a gaunt, gray, hollow-eyed creature, listless and ill-tempered, prone to headaches and itching and sudden waves of pain—and my hair was shot through with this wild streak of white. Because of the pain, and the morphia injections I had to have to control it, my arms were like pincushions, the punctures crowded together in rashes. I'd already been told that Henry Bird was dead, which did little to help, but as I say, at this stage I still believed in your mother, and remembered our last conversation, when she'd so deftly dispelled my feelings of guilt about him. I was even able to handle the shock of having Vincent Cushing come and tell me quite bluntly that I wouldn't be required on his service any longer. Even this I could cope with, for I'd already anticipated Ratcliff talking to him, urging my dismissal—and getting his way, for of course he shared with Cushing a near-impregnable position high in the hierarchy of St. Basil's. The shame of it was, of course, that I couldn't say a word in my own defense. I couldn't accuse him of knocking me down the stairs, because that would have dragged your mother into it, which was unthinkable. But yes, I could cope with it, because I thought she loved me, believed in me, and was waiting for me.

I was in traction for six weeks, and it was another six weeks before I was able to bear weight on my leg.

I changed. During those terrible weeks, I changed. The gaunt gray man who limped out of St. Basil's in the summer of 1938 was a very different creature from the passionate fellow who'd stood his ground that spring and told the senior pathologist what harm he was doing his wife. Suffering leaves its mark; what is it Wordsworth says?

> Suffering is permanent, obscure and dark,
> And shares the nature of infinity.

My suffering was certainly permanent; as to its darkness and obscurity, your mother's rejection was the single worst shock I had to bear—all of it I could have endured without faltering, had she remained true. She did not; and though my love did not abate in the slightest—it grew stronger, in fact—I was forced to go forward alone. This tempered me. It matured me. I aged many years in those short weeks, learned much about the spirit and about that pear-shaped, fist-sized, four-chambered bag we call the human heart. Poetry, you see, was my great aid, in those dark nights, to know that what I was experiencing had been experienced before, and by men who could transmute that experience into beauty:

> Most wretched men
> Are cradled into poetry by wrong;
> They learn in suffering what they teach in song.

James, fallen angel: this is my song.

I still possess the letter she sent me. I'd intended one day to show it to you, but I don't suppose it matters now. It was shattering. I believe it would have devastated me even if I'd been in rude good health. It would have devastated any man. It didn't say much. We were never to see each other again. I was to keep my promise not to try and make her change her mind. It could never work for us—surely, she wrote, I must have known that? She had a son, a home, a marriage. It was over. No tenderness. No word of love. The first time I read it was like being struck full force in the face with a bucket of cold seawater. Spike started up immediately, and I had to shout for McGuinness though he'd seen to me only an hour before. What was I to do? What could I do? I smelled the hand of Ratcliff all over that letter. It was all too easy to imagine her situation: he would answer the telephone, intercept the mail, watch her like a hawk; any attempt on my part would only make things worse. I wasn't afraid of Ratcliff, don't think that. Despite what he'd done to me, don't think that. But I was afraid of what he might do to your mother, should I disobey her instructions.

I did on one occasion telephone her. It was the middle of the afternoon, so Ratcliff was almost certainly down in Pathology. I made my way on crutches to the end of the ward and the public telephone. In my dressing gown and slippers, and weak with pain and apprehension, I dialed the number. It was picked up on the fourth ring. "Yes?" she said. How flat her voice was. Devoid of expression, achingly, pathetically empty of feeling—this was what he'd brought her to. "It's me," I said, "can you talk?"

"Who is this?"

"Edward."

"Oh." A long pause. Then: "Yes?"

"I got your letter. I know you didn't mean it."

"I'm afraid I can't talk to you," she said in that cold, dead voice, and hung up the receiver. She was sealed off from me, in some grim prison of Ratcliff's making. The next afternoon a rather sinister thing happened. Lying on my bed, I realized that he was standing at the end of the ward in a black rubber apron with his sleeves rolled up, staring straight at me. Then he was at my bedside! "You little fool, she doesn't want you," he hissed, "don't you understand that? *She doesn't want you!*" I tried to raise my head from the pillow but could not—the effort exhausted me—I was drenched in sweat—a wave of nausea swept over me—and when I opened my eyes again he was gone. She'd told him, then. I didn't try to reach her again.

Oh, I thought about it. I thought for a time it was my duty to reach her, to somehow get her away from Ratcliff and make her see what he was doing to her; I couldn't forget the tone of her voice when she'd said, "I'm afraid I can't talk to you." They echoed in my head, those dead flat tones, during the pain-racked days and nights I spent in St. Basil's, they devastated me, and it was a week before I finally began to attempt to accept the fact that I had to let her go. I have to

123

let her go, I have to let her go: up and down the ward I'd hobble on my crutches, the words like the chant of a mob in my head, you have to let her go, you have to let her go—armies marching acros Europe, and as they marched they chanted, you have to let her go, you have to let her go. "But I *cannot* let her go!"—I awoke one night with this scream on my lips, and woke the ward (what's worse I woke Spike too), but it did no good, those marching armies just kept on and on and on: you have to let her go, you have to let her go.

Eventually I was discharged from St. Basil's. I was getting about with just the aid of a stick by this time; the pain was still bad, and the scuffed leather medical kit I carried containing needle and ampoules was, if not the center of my existence, certainly necessary for my sense of security. I'd accepted the inevitable, and felt as though a loved one had died: I was in a state of mourning. My interest in the outside world was nil, and I was incapable of activity. I spent my days and nights shuffling wretchedly about my room in Jubilee Road, glancing into volumes of poetry only to toss them aside with weary indifference. I knew I would never love again. I would never do anything again. All I could do was grieve.

I told myself to forget her, but I thought about her constantly. Everything reminded me of her. The lamps. The rug. The fly-in-glass in my trouser pocket—I kept it over on Spike's side, they somehow seemed connected, Spike and the fly. I'd take it out a dozen times a day and turn it in my fingers till the sobs came, till the grief racked me anew, and that would get Spike going, and I'd have to reach for the scuffed leather medical kit to deal with the pain, for the one pain unfailingly engendered the other, as though a current flowed from heart to hip, and hip to heart. The Keats she gave me, which we'd read from together in front of the fire—it was practically crystalline with associations, as was the porcelain vase, the flowers (I never let Mrs. Kelly throw out her flowers)—dead now, these many weeks, and their water stinking, but I gathered the brittle fallen petals in a saucer and gazed at them for hours on end: *for she had touched them!* Her voice was in my dreams, though I hardly slept at all, but the semiconscious daze I'd slip into, after relieving Spike—it was then that I was most susceptible to her presence, the sound of her voice, her footfall on the landing outside my door—I'd heave up out of my chair at dead of night, and with the grotesque gait, part limp, part lurch, of the agitated cripple, haul myself over to the door and fling it wide and there'd be—nothing!

Nothing. I sank deeper into listless depression. It occurred to me that if I brought up the memory of every occasion on which we'd been together—what we'd done, what we'd said—I could somehow rob them of their power to ravage and devastate me. I could defuse them. It did no good. Worse: it exacerbated the pain, which got Spike going, so I'd have to have a shot, and then I'd hear her, and so it started all over again.

I was going mad.

I had to do something—good God, I had to make a living! I forced myself to face facts. A career in surgery was no longer a possiblity, so I had to think about general medicine. Positions in London were few, but I could easily enough find work as an assistant in some country practice and make five hundred pounds a year. And given all that had happened, given my state of mind, the idea of getting out of London actually roused, for the first time in weeks, a small faint flicker of interest—until, that is, the reality of country practice came home to me. Was this really the best I could hope for? The promising young doctor who'd won a coveted place at one of the great London teaching hospitals—was I now to become an overworked, underpaid assistant to some country doctor? It rather looked as though I was.

This provoked fresh despair, lassitude, self-reproach. I was worthless and despicable, and I deserved all the misfortune that had befallen me. I had never been anything but worthless and despicable, and it was impossible that your mother could ever have loved me. She was right to reject me. I was incapable of love, I was incapable of achieving anything of value, I was petty, narcissistic, dishonest, weak, and my one sole aim had always been to hide my weakness—this seemed undeniably true, for apparently I was now addicted to morphia as well. It only surprised me that I should have had to be brought so low to recognize it.

The salient feature of those days, then, a profound dissatisfaction with myself which, when it became particularly acute, set off Spike, which then had me reaching for my medical kit, and in the brief dreamy hours of release that followed your mother would become vividly present to me, which would set the whole sorry train in motion once more. The dead, flat creature caught in a prison, and powerless to escape, was not, I then realized, your mother—it was me. No wonder she rejected me. Such were my thoughts. And any pity I may have felt for her, should, I saw, in justice, have been directed toward myself: it was *I* who was weak and powerless! Thus I railed at myself, thus did I make myself suffer, and in the process derived a sick, self-punitive gratification. It occurred to me at one point that if I died your mother would then, at least, be forced to acknowledge what I'd felt for her, and what she had sacrificed. Oh, I was an open wound, and without sleep I could not heal.

I realized that the first thing was to get off the morphia. Spike hurt, this was a fact of life, even after bony union was effected in my hip; and he hurt worst as I fell off to sleep, when my muscles relaxed and the damaged bone ground like a drill against its seating in the pelvis. A needle relieved that hurt, not only relieved it but brought in its train waves of peace and serenity—nonetheless I couldn't use morphia as a crutch for the rest of my life, with God knows what effect upon my moral and intellectual functioning. So I stopped. One morning I just stopped.

At first all was well. I had risen at my usual time and

gone without my morning shot, and spent the next hours looking at the newspaper. It was around noon—twelve hours after the last injection—that I began to grow uneasy. I became aware that a feeling of weakness had gradually crept over me. I began to yawn, then noticed that I couldn't stop shivering. I pulled a blanket round my shoulders. I seemed to be weeping, though not out of misery, it wasn't true weeping, it was, rather, a hot, watery discharge that had begun pouring from my eyes and nose in a copious stream. I crawled into bed—that huge creaky bed I had shared so often with *her*!—and fell into a restless sleep.

Throughout that warm summer afternoon I tossed and turned under the sheet and was tormented by grotesque dreams. I saw Ratcliff bearing down on me in his black rubber apron; his face a rictus of rage and in his hand an amputation knife. I found myself on the steel table in the postmortem room with Ratcliff and Miggs and Cushing sniggering down at me. My thorax was open, my insides were piled neatly on my chest, and my penis was rolling around on the floor. I got up on one elbow, concerned to recover my penis, and my insides slithered off and fell on the floor and they all laughed.

I awoke at six in the evening: eighteen hours since the last injection. I couldn't stop yawning—I yawned so violently I feared I would dislocate my jaw. Armies of ants crawled about under my skin. Huddled in my blanket with the tears pouring from my eyes, and a watery mucus from my nose, I managed with difficulty to smoke a cigarette. I was shivering uncontrollably.

At one point I struggled to the fireplace and peered at myself in the mirror. My pupils were dilated and the skin of my face was pimpled like gooseflesh. Suddenly I felt violently sick. There was no time to reach the bathroom down the hall, I had to make do with my chamber pot. The vomiting was explosive. Its contents were streaked with blood. Kneeling there over my bloody flux I opened my shirt and saw the skin of my belly knotted and corrugated as though a nest of vipers were writhing beneath it. Diarrhea soon followed. But I did not crack.

The hours crawled by. I called your mother's name, it gave me strength. I was doing it for her, this was the only way I could go on with it. By the next morning I was in truly pitiful condition. In a desperate attempt to relieve the chills racking me I had gone back to bed and covered myself with every blanket I could lay my hands on. My whole body shook and twitched beneath this mountain of bedclothes, though the pain not only in my hip but in all my muscles prevented me from getting sleep or even rest. I clambered out of bed and for a while I limped back and forth across the room, attempting to get warm. I opened a book and tried to read; hopeless of course. With tears of frustration and misery I climbed back into bed: the sheets and blankets were soaked through to the mattress. Then came a knock at the door! Filthy, unshaven, befouled with vomit, I called through the door: "Who is it?" My voice was a weak, fluty thing, like an old man's. I was only just able to keep the concerned Desmond Kelly from coming in to see what was the matter.

Time passed with excruciating slowness, and no relief came. I could neither eat or drink, and in the course of that second day I became weaker and weaker as my bodily reserves were consumed and vitality slipped away. I thought then that unless I found relief I would surely die; and that seemed a heavy price to pay for dispensing with a crutch. Shortly after noon I broke. I cracked. I barely had the energy to drag myself out of my armchair and with trembling fingers make up a needle. But thirty minutes later (so rapid was my recovery) I was downstairs shaved, clean, and joking weakly with Desmond Kelly about the terrible noises he'd heard from my room in the night. Eight hours after that I felt again the unease that had ushered in the nightmare, and I decided to prolong my holiday from hell. As I have ever since.

Three days later there again came a knock at the door. It was early evening and the light was starting to go. Desmond Kelly stood there with a letter. I tore it open. It was from Hugh Fig, the solicitor in Griffin Head. Apparently Henry's will had been read: everything was left to me, including the house. I looked up—gazed with a dawning smile into the mild, sad face of Desmond Kelly—and in that moment knew I was saved. In the midst of my darkness had come this one pure blessed shaft of grace. Despite all I'd done to him, Henry had kept faith with me. Grace, unbidden, had entered in, and my next steps were obvious, certain, and natural.

STRETCHING IT
WIDER

John Giorno

Some things
that work
in one
decade,
don't work
in the next,
so mark
it down
as a noble
idea
that failed.

And I did
what everybody
dreams
of doing,
I walked
away
from it
I walked away
from it
I walked away from it
I walked away from it,
and I never
went back,
without reconcile.

132

And since I
can't leave,
I love
getting drunk
with you
I love getting
drunk with you
I love getting drunk with you,
and give me some
more blow.

Nobody
ever gives
you what
you want
except by mistake,

and the only
things you
ever got
is what
you did for yourself,
cause you
hate them
and you're only
doing it
everyday
for the money,
you hate them
and you're only doing it
everyday for the money.

I know guys
who work
all their
life
and have got
alot,
and something
happens to him,
and he loses
everything
just like that,
and I haven't
even got
that
and I haven't even got that.

Hard
work,
low
pay,
and embarrassing
conditions,
you are worse
than I remember,
and you're
home
and you're home
and you're home
and you're home
and you're home.

134

What is
a rat doing,
when it
isn't eating
garbage
or scaring you
on the street,
they're laying
around
like pussy cats,
you and I
sleeping in
the bed sheets,
warm
and cozy
sliding

your legs
under the covers
and staying there.

You got to keep
down
cause they're shooting
low,
press your body
against the ground,
it's gravity,
the telephone
hasn't rung
once today.

If there is
one thing
you can not
and will not
do
is make
this world
a better
place,
if there's one thing
you can't do
is make the world
a better place,
if there's one thing
you're not going to do
is make the world a better place.

Cause you are
only successful
when you
rip
somebody off,
and everybody
I've ever known
who wants to
help somebody,
wants to
help themself,
and I'm a firm
believer in
giving somebody
136   enough rope
to hang themself.

You're standing here
watching all
these people,
and everything seems
a little
confused
and everything seems
a little confused,
I haven't got
anything to say.

The noose
is tightening
the noose is tightening

the noose is tightening,
and let me make
one more
further
observation,
when you
die,
you're going to die
with a hard-on.

If I didn't
have an
accident
I wouldn't
be here
If I didn't have
an accident
I wouldn't be here
If I didn't have an accident
I wouldn't be here.

Then there is
the reality
of the family,
your mother
and father,
them and
my mistakes
is why
I'm sitting
at a table

with a bunch
of stupid
jerks
on Thanksgiving
eating
a turkey
stuffed
with lasagna.

I'm spending
my whole
life
being with
people
138 I don't want
to be with
I spending my whole
life being with people
I don't want to be with
I spending my whole life
being with people
I don't want to be with,
and there ain't
no such thing
as family,
just people
you work with.

I love
completely
perverted

people,
you are my
best
sexual
fantasy,

I never got
that far with
scat
before
and I want to
remember it,
tireless
and I want to remember it,
tireless
and I want to remember it, tireless.

139

We make money
the old-fashioned
way,
we earn it,
the anchor
man
never leaves
the building,
and the only
difference
between me
and a preacher,
is he's
telling you

he has a way
out,
and I'm telling you
don't bother,
for you
there is
no way
out
for you there
is no way out
for you there is no
way out
for you there is no way out,
and it isn't
140 as though
you got anything
to lose.

Besides they
blocked
permanantly
all
the exits
they blocked permanently
all the exits,
you and I
get to
stay here
forever
and it gets
worse

beyond your
imagination.

I would like
to give my
best
to all sentient
beings,
and before
I die,
I'd like
to de-tox
my mind
and tame
delusion,
but we are not
in a time
appropriate
to do this.

Tonight,
I want you
to give us
some drugs
and a little
alcohol,
if something
is good
people
like it
if something is good

people like it
if something is good people like it.

It looks
the way
it should
and you make me
feel good,
so let's
open it
up,
stretching it
wider
stretching
142   it wider
stretching it wider
stretching it wider
stretching it
wider,
and it shouldn't be
any trouble.
                    1982

THE OTHER WORLD

John Wynne

THE GROCERY CARTS were scattered over the lot. He could already feel his hands forced against the hot bars. *Goddam people*, Pete thought, *leave 'em anywhere*. He packed the last sack with bananas, cereal and Cokes. Then he glanced up at the booth and, of course, Mr. Raney was giving him the nod. Pete nodded back, wiped his hands on his apron and stepped outside. The sun hit him full in the face. He couldn't find a breath of air that wasn't wet or heavy or yellow. He started rounding up the carts. The scenery wasn't so bad today. A band of girls was heading home from the Dairy Queen. They carried foamy whipped sodas and chocolate-dipped cones. They wore shorts.

Tight. Their legs had soft white hairs. He liked one of the girls. Ruby Lacy. Her tongue darted out to save the melting chocolate. He felt his stomach get all tight. He jerked the baskets away from the Buick just in time, but the old man still yelled, "Watch where you're goin', will ya?" Back inside, Pete chose to stock the canned milk so he could bend down and see up the girls' skirts. Ray was left to the higher shelves. "Better keep the radio down, old man Raney might come round any minute." But Ray kept flipping stations. Sweet and creamy pop sounds. There was a special song he was looking for. Something about love on a rooftop. "That's a real old one," Pete insisted. "No, it ain't. I hear it in the halls at school all the time." "Just keep it way low . . ." Canned milk cans. Pete wiped his forehead.

At dinner no one spoke much. Florence wiped the pudding off Michael's chin. "Mom," Pete said. Florence smiled and raised her head. "How long usually before a first paycheck?" She fed another spoonful to the baby. "I don't know, dear. I just don't know." Pete stared. He hated her hair that way, those thin beige strands swept up into an old-fashioned bun. His father finished his hamsteak. His brother, James, sat dreaming into space. "I mowed the entire lawn today," Rich Grady said. "You boys can do the trimming. Is it a deal?" "Sure, Dad." "Yeah, Dad." Pete thought bitterly that James didn't even have a summer job—why, he should do all the trimming himself. "Where is Carol tonight?" Florence asked James. "She's studying for her biology exam." "That girl is such a good student." Florence got the last of the bean pudding down the baby's throat.

At ten, Pete wasn't sleepy. There wasn't much to read except the encyclopedia. He chose Vol. 15 MARY to MUS and almost choked when he came upon a big color picture of MODERN DRAMATIC MASKS—"mural paintings by Wladyslaw T. Benda showing the dramatic use of masks as they are employed in grotesque painting." His blood swelled, his heart beat swiftly. There was a naked woman surrounded by eight creatures and a lion. But the eight creatures were part human. Pete was stunned to see some had webbed feet and hands, some had long noses and gaping mouths, and one was a skeleton with wings. The naked woman stood in the middle and they were staring at her, ready to prey upon her. Some had nice strong bodies, they looked awfully well-built to Pete, and their muscles rippled under red satin. She wore a peacock plume for a headdress. She was naked running suspended one foot suddenly immobile. Pete felt himself getting hard. His mother came into the room, and Pete slammed the encyclopedia shut. "Your grandmother may be coming to stay the weekend."

The weather wasn't any better and the carts were spread about as usual. Pete and Ray flipped a coin to see who would collect them. Today it was Ray. At lunch Pete sat in the back and talked to Weedy, who cut meat. Pete was working on a big provolone hero Gladys Morgan made for him. "That looks good," Weedy said. "Pretty tasty." "Know why I say that, kid?" Wham. "No." "Because it don't have no meat in it." Wham. Two chicken legs, big ones, severed from the body. "Sometimes I sure get sick of this. Wait till they start giving their orders. These people, they don't know what they want." That picture kept coming back to Pete fast as waves in a rainbow. Wham. In waves.

Florence ironed her blouse. "James, there's nothing better than doing simple things. Nothing in the world. Your mind doesn't get a chance to wander. First a shirt, then an apron, then a dress, then some linen. No time to wander, James. And if it does . . . even for a moment . . . it only wanders above." She did Michael's things, bibs and overalls. "Bibs that don't come clean as they should," she sang.

146   Pete watched t.v. at Robby Martin's house. It was a color t.v. The woman's face was blue with green fringe around it. Pete fiddled with the dial. The color was still a little off. Better now. Soon though, her face got blue again. Pete slammed his fist against the table. "Why in hell did you do that for?" Robby asked. "I don't know." "Well, look out. You'll splinter the wood, then I'll get blamed for it." "Shut up, anyway." "Make me." Pete jumped off the couch and tackled Robby, knocking him to the floor. He pinned him down and pressed on him with all his weight. "Get off — you're killing me!" But Pete rubbed his face into the rug. "Give . . .?" Robby spluttered. "No . . . I can't get my breath!" Pete didn't realize he could pin Robby that easily. He didn't realize his own strength. Robby's face was bright red and he was struggling in vain. Pete was a foot from the t.v. screen. She was in front of him

and had started to sing. There was a chorus of men behind her in white coats giving those toothy smiles. "Get up—you're killing me . . ." Close-up of her face. Green with blue fringe. Pete felt himself getting hard. He felt for a minute she was under him. Then he realized it was Robby still squirming. Pete rolled off, embarrassed that Robby might have felt him get hard. But Robby didn't say anything. Nothing. He just lay there panting gut heaving her picture above his head. Then they cut away to some man talking.

"Happy birthday!" "Happy birthday, son." "Happy birthday, Pete." "Sixteen candles for my child." "For our strong boy, Mama." Ribbons. Sweaters. Butter-scotch ice cream. A hunting knife from his father. "Sixteen candles for our big boy." But later in his room, Pete trembled as he fingered the package he had hidden under his mattress—the only birthday present he really wanted. And he had given it to himself. He had sent away six weeks ago using one of those order blanks from the back page of a comic book. He had bitten his nails past his skin in those weeks, waiting. Finally, his grandmother had answered the door on a rainy afternoon to find the postman holding the carefully wrapped parcel. She paid the C.O.D. charges, dried off the package and left it in his room. He had saved this moment for when he was in his bedroom alone and everybody else was asleep. He cut the strings with his birthday knife. There they were. His new masks. Remarkably lifelike, supple. Six of them. Sylvester Stallone, Batman, the Creature from the Black Lagoon, a death skull, a wolf salivating,

and a laughing fat lady. The last ones were cheapo
plastic jobs, and the laughing fat lady looked down-
right shabby. He slipped on the Stallone and turned
to the mirror. Real lifelike. Covered his whole face.
He pictured himself stepping right out of *Rambo*. He
even found a comb and pretended to give the slicked-
back hair a careless stroke or two. Then he tried the
death's head. Vacant eyes, rotted, corn-colored teeth,
and a black widow crawling from the left socket. He
hadn't realized he'd unzipped his pants and been jer-
king off, but now his hand was covered with sperm,
some of it was even running along the mirror, and a
tiring kind of thrill engulfed him, encouraging him to
whisper aloud, "If there were seven steps to hell, I'd
take them."

Florence tapped the table. "She's a godsend, that
woman." "Who?" She tapped the table again emphatically. "Phyllis Schlafly, James. Look at her picture on
the cover of *Christian Family* . . . it doesn't matter if
she's married because a woman like that is really the
bride of Christ . . . She exudes . . . well, she simply
exudes . . . holiness . . . ness. That sounds sacred,
doesn't it, that double s at the end? . . . *Holy* is one
sound, but *ness* is another. She and Reverend Falwell
are trying to put a stop to this sickness that you, of
course, don't know exists." "Yes, I do, Mother. When
two people of the same sex love each other. Carol
doesn't think there's anything wrong with that."
Florence raised her eyebrows. "She doesn't?" she
asked in a wondering tone. She did think so much of

Carol and wondered if Carol might know something she didn't.

He cut off the head of the chicken and wiped his brow. "Eating meat today, huh, kid?" "Yeah." "Well, I'm gonna swipe me some lime Jell-o—California Jell-o salad, I think it's called. Don't give me away, huh?" "Sure, Weedy." Pete looked out through the two-way mirror at the meat market. He had been told to keep his eyes open for shoplifters during his lunch hour and if he caught one he'd make ten dollars. He hoped that once he might catch a young girl but he hadn't yet. There he was again. That poor boy with dirt on his face and his legs all scarred. He had an expression of a fox, caught and wounded, but who somehow enjoyed being in the trap even though he hurt. His presence upset Pete. He always seemed to hang around the store in the afternoons. Barefoot and usually bleeding. From what, Pete couldn't figure out. The kid couldn't have been more than nine. One day Pete saw him bend over by the Cokes and Pepsis and set his toes on fire. Pete couldn't believe it. Struck a match and lit his toes. When Pete pounded on the glass, the kid blew on his flesh and a little gray puff of smoke came up and the kid ran. He was raving mad, Pete decided.

Florence looked into her baby's eyes. "You're baptized. Praise be God." Pete shut the encyclopedia. *Ruby Lacy, Ruby Lacy. When you see me next you'll be half crazy.*

She lived at 1485 Wyoming Street in a small wood house with a ton of acorns rotting on the roof. There was a rotting tree next to it from which a family of squirrels had easy access to the roof. Pete knew her father had deserted her mother years ago and that just the two of them shared the house. Her mother worked until five and Ruby usually got home at four after an ice cream cone with her girlfriends. The house was not on a busy road so there was nobody to see him peeping in the windows. The squirrels kept kicking the nuts off the roof with their back feet. Once when a car passed, he bent over and picked some up. He could hide his face that way. Ruby had gone from her bedroom to the bathroom and Pete took the opportunity to climb in the window. He stood behind her door and put on the Stallone mask. He could hear

her flush the toilet and go into the kitchen. The high tinkling of the spoon told him she was making a glass of ice tea. He figured there was no other sound in the world quite like that. Footsteps. She was coming. When she had crossed the room, he kicked the door shut behind her. She turned to see a stranger in a mask holding a knife casually in front of him. The glass of ice tea dropped from her hands. Shattered. She forgot to scream her feet were in pain she kept stepping back and forth on the glass. The voice said, "Take your pants off and you won't get hurt. Call for help and you're dead." Ruby pulled down her blue jeans going back and forth on one foot then the other. "Now lie on the bed." The mask looked stern, brows crossed somewhat apprehensively, but there was a look of concern around the eyes. In a minute, he was on top of her, spreading her legs. He pinned her hands behind her and held them with one hand, with the other he beat her. Pete was behind the mask and he felt himself slide into her. He hit her in the face. "Please do anything, just quit hitting me." Once she pried a hand loose and dug him with her fingernails as hard as she could. But Sylvester Stallone's face didn't bleed. No defense.

At home, Pete put the mask under the mattress and changed clothes. He took a shower. He felt he never wanted to do that again at the same time wanting to do it all over again. He knew no one had seen him. He was a quick jogger. People saw him run home every day after school.

Ruby didn't come back to class until November. Pete was never more excited than on the day she returned. Her face was still bruised, but what was worse, she could hardly move without crutches, her feet swathed in heavy bandages. The cuts. He couldn't resist going up to her between classes. "Ruby, what in the world happened to you?" She answered with a restless look in her eye. "I was in a car accident." "Oh," Pete sympathized. "Not too bad, I hope." She paused. "Oh, no, it looks worse than it is." Pete knew there had been a couple of other "car accidents" since Ruby's and that he had been responsible. He wondered why they hadn't admitted what had happened. Soon the fact that they kept it a secret made him angry. He wanted to put a hole into somebody so deep it would burn right through their clothes.

Wham. "Today your sandwich makes me puke," Weedy said. Even though school was back in full swing, Pete managed to keep his job part-time. Though he regretted the cold days, he never regretted the extra money.

There was only a thin layer of frost on the yard and it wasn't cold so Pete thought nothing of sitting there after dinner. James came up behind him acting like it was the craziest stunt he could imagine. "What do you think we have heaters for, anyway?" "When I get cold, I'll come in." James sat down on the steps. "Gee, you can even see your breath." Pete just wished he would leave him alone. "Pete, did you know I was accepted at college for the fall?" "No . . . that's wonderful." "Well, you see, I'm the first one in my family to go. I am proud about it. Now Carol and I can go together." James looked into Pete's eyes. "Pete . . ." "Yeah?" "Well . . . I hope you don't think I'm trying to be nosy . . . but . . ." Pete suddenly got very cold and he shivered. He shifted weight. "What do you want to say to me, James?" He was surprised to hear his voice shake. "How are your grades this semester, any better?" Pete let out his breath. "Yeah, much better." "That's good because you want to go to college like me, don't you?" "Yeah, I do." "That makes me happy. Mom and Dad weren't too sure about it, whether you wanted to go or not, but we all want you to go to a good college with values, good moral, no, I don't mean to say that, but someplace that isn't, you know, I don't know . . ." "It's not for another year, anyway." "But we have to think ahead and keep our grades up."

It was the first time her parents had been away the

whole year. They had gone up north to see her mother's sick sister. They planned to be back by Tuesday. She couldn't go with them because of student teaching. James drove Carol home. Pete could see him take her up to the door. Her figure shone in the headlights. The garage smelled like spilled milk instead of oil. He wiped his shoes against the wood to be sure they weren't sticky. She let herself in and then James drove away. Pete slipped on his mask. He'd chosen the wolf, he liked it best at night because it was so scary. It even scared him sometimes, it was so ugly. Carol sat at the dining room table, grading papers. Pete figured his paper was with the rest. He crawled in her bedroom window then crouched in the hall. When she got up to go to the kitchen, he sprang at her full force. Her face was so full of terror that for a moment she looked a hundred years old. Pete slugged her in the stomach to knock the wind out of her so she couldn't cry out, then he yanked the floor lamp and threw it in the kitchen. Darkness. He lifted her up then dropped her on top of the table. Her back hit the wood with a deep thud. Then he raped her. When he left he figured she must be hurt because she hardly moved. Back home he looked at the mask. It was fearsome. Carol never talked much about that night. As far as he knew, she never told James the truth. She had slipped and fallen and broken her back and had to be in traction for eight months.

153

Pete worked late sometimes. Mr. Raney had the choice of either Ray or Pete and he always picked Pete. Pete didn't mind. He enjoyed the night work, stocking shelves, etc. He was now arranging the tomato pastes. Suddenly the lights in the store went out. One by one. It was eerie. Pete looked up. There in the booth sat Mr. Raney, the only light in the place on his desk. He motioned for Pete to come in. Pete took off his apron and slowly made his way. There was something about Mr. Raney today. He coughed for no reason. He avoided Pete when usually he was on his back. His face was lighter than a ghost's. "Close the door behind you . . . like a good boy." Pete felt funny. "Come close . . . Pete." Pete stood right in the light. Raney sat behind him in his swivel chair, his account book on the desk.

"I'm going over my business, Pete . . . it's been a profitable year. People will pay anything for food, you know. That's one thing they can't do without." Raney chuckled and Pete didn't like the sound. "Come here." "I can't come any closer, Mr. Raney, or I'd be sitting on your lap." That chuckle again. "But, my boy, that's what I want you to do . . . sit . . ." Raney spread his legs and put his arms around Pete's waist and gently eased him down. Pete squirmed. He hated it. Raney was twice his size. He felt trapped, he wasn't used to feeling this way. "Pete . . . ," he whispered, "I'm glad you came to Daddy." The light showed a small hole in Raney's pants. Pete couldn't help staring. "Oh, that?" said Raney. "My wife did it. She's a good woman, Pete, a wonderful wife. But she dropped her cigarette as she was ironing 'em . . . you know what she did then? She broke into tears and said, 'Oh, God, we don't have any little boy, Homer, we don't have any!' And I cried with her and I told her, 'Honey, there's this boy at my store . . . I think of him as a son.' I do. I do, Pete. Yeah, you're my son. I always wanted a son . . ." Tears swelled. "To do all the things boys like to do . . . play baseball . . . learn to hunt . . . ride a bike . . . play football . . . basketball . . ." His voice cracked. "The things everybody else does but me!" Pete got up. "Do you think you would like to come by, Pete, just say one night a week . . . one night a week to start, that is . . . and have dinner with me and my wife?" Pete was out the door. Raney screamed and pounded the desk, tears falling from his face, "I want to go fishing, damn it!"

The laughing fat lady. Pete pulled it from his back pocket. He was so full of hatred for Raney that he knew he could do what he didn't want to do. He thought Mrs. Raney was uglier than sin, but he could pretend she was somebody else. He stood by the bushes fiddling with the mask. He finally tightened it around his face. Then he saw her. Mrs. Raney. Sitting at the window staring at him. Impossible. He thought he had heard her in the back. But no. She was right at the window sitting as if she hadn't moved all day. She was looking at him with . . . mild curiosity. Pete realized she knew who he was. After all, she must have seen his face. He ripped off the mask and bolted away. He ran home faster than he had ever run before. He collided with his father in the middle of the front yard. "Hey . . ." Rich Grady's deep voice. He cupped Pete on the shoulder. "You go way too fast." Pete gasped. The police must be after him. There was wild

155

fear in his face but Rich didn't seem to notice. Pete ran to his room and hid the mask. He fell on his bed and prayed to God that he wouldn't be caught. Soon he was able to breathe again yet he kept thinking, *She saw me . . . she saw me*. Time passed and no police came. The only voice was Florence's as she gibbered with the baby. Then she called him to dinner. *Wait a minute*, he thought. *She probably doesn't know about the other girls . . . she might have thought I was some kid . . . with a mask. Yeah, just some kid with a mask*. And he hoped against hope that he was right.

Florence went to the beauty parlor only once a year. The day of the annual picnic. "So early in the spring," she sang as she left the shop. They had done a beautiful job. She looked so presentable. The little brook by the church glowed crisply in the sunlight. Reverend Orry embraced her. "You look wonderful. And not even a sweater." "Oh, no, Reverend. Not on such a Godlike day!" "How right you are." The boys were playing along the brook. "Precious." "More than precious," he corrected her. "Human. Human, but they breathe the breath of God." Florence smoothed her dress. It was a floral print. She looked at the trees. Apple blossoms. Shed by the hundreds. "The smell of spring." "Yes, Florence, it is indeed the smell of spring." The boys ran along the water's edge. "Florence . . . what ideas as a Christian can you offer to see these boys go with God?" Florence thought. "Well, we really can't be happy or at peace without a solid foundation at home, can we, Reverend?" "Indeed, not, child." "And I think what concerns most

Christian mothers is the breakdown of family life. I think the issue of homosexuality is important when our children are at stake . . . I certainly want to keep them away from my boys, Pete and James . . . and those boys out there . . . I want to keep them away!" "We must. But Florence, you are a good wife and mother. As a woman, you don't have to look so far." "I don't understand, Reverend." "Have you noticed that women seem to have lost their sense of certainty in this age? They say they want more rights, even though they already can kill their own babies. How dare they bring the curse of degradation upon us with these so-called rights? A woman in this town, excuse me for being outspoken, wrote the newspaper that she saw no problem in women sharing public toilets with men." "I can't believe it, nor do I understand it." "Can you think for a minute, Florence, can you think what that means?" Florence was puzzled. "You mean . . .?" "Just think, that's all, just think." There was an excited shout from the boys. Florence and Reverend Orry saw that they had just hit a frog with a big stone exactly on target. They walked on. "The bells in the church sound musical, Reverend. Very musical. Each time I hear them, I remember to feed the baby. And I think, *His little ears are hearing this too.* Isn't that a funny thought?" "Yes, but it's thoughts like that coming and going that sometimes lead us to a profound discovery . . . something we had no idea was important at the time. You know, I'm now reminded of someone very dear to me who has gone to her reward. Rose Hart, an old-time evangelist, used to come to these

157

spring picnics year after year, and she'd go around and ask everybody, 'Have you ever had a message from The Other World?' And one day I said, 'Yes, Sister, I have,' for I finally saw what she meant." The evening air was warm yet there was something bracing about it. Florence hurried along the sidewalk. She was in such a good mood she was almost skipping. She laughed to herself once, just as the sun slid over the roofs of the parked cars. She had been thinking, *What would Jesus think if He came back to earth today? He would most likely be horrified. And He would be confused about the sharing of the toilets because He wouldn't know what they were used for since they didn't have them in his time!* Florence hugged herself. *Yes, I'll have to teach Jesus about the toilets.* She stepped off the curb into the path of a Honda Accord. The driver tried to brake but it was all so sudden. She was killed instantly, that was a mercy to the family. The driver felt so badly he came to the funeral. He explained to Pete and James and to Rich, "God forgive me, there was nothing I could do." The lid came down on the coffin. Pete crossed himself as they laid his mother in the grave.

Several nights later the men ate a lonely dinner. Finally Rich Grady broke the silence and in his usual stern, unquavering voice, he said, "Listen. I want you boys to understand this. This house still has a sense of order ... a sense of decency. Your mother and I discussed if something like this ever happened—you were not to think of her anymore as Florence ... she wants you to think of her as Mary. You understand?" Pete wondered why the lights were turned off in the living and dining rooms while they ate. The light in the kitchen lit the table indirectly. Harshly. The next night he flipped on the other lights and no one took exception so he guessed everybody had just forgotten. Pete learned to change Michael's diapers. He didn't like the job but his father insisted. One night the baby screamed bloody murder. Pete thought then of raping somebody.

On Friday he came home from school, threw his books on his desk and flopped onto the bed. He put his hands under the mattress to pull out The Creature from the Black Lagoon. His fingers only felt the springs. Desperately he pushed his hands farther under. Nothing. He leaped off the bed and pulled the mattress up. Gone. All of them. Who had found them? His father? Brother? Pete was in shock. He broke into a cold sweat. He fell in front of the mirror and prayed that everything would be all right. Then he told his father he had a stomachache, which was true, and got into bed for the night. He woke in the dark from a terrible dream. He found he was crying. He never never wanted to have that dream again. He had heard something in the basement. "Who's there?" No answer. He turned on the flashlight and walked slowly from his room. He walked and walked for hours, past all familiar objects in his house, but now he lingered over each one with microscopic eyes even though he was moving all the time. Gliding, shuddering, knowing what he would find when he opened the door. Finally that moment came. The bright beam of the flashlight. The door springing back. From the depths

159

of the basement wandered that poor boy from the store, a hunk of concrete torn out of the wall where he had been chained. His arm was still tightly bound and little worms of blood popped around the metal. He came up the stairs, plaster and blood in his hair, a cruel, defiant smile on his lips. He was grateful to Pete for rescuing him ... but even more grateful to Pete for having chained him. Pete woke with a cry. The dream faded.

The next morning brought the sun and with it a new strength. The cobwebs and tired old spiders were brushed away along with the moon and stars. Pete thought of a girl and her eleven-year-old sister who lived near the woods. They never took the bus. They had a leisurely country breakfast and then walked to school. He thought of grabbing them from behind a tree before they had a chance to rub the sleep from their eyes. He looked down the hall. The door to his mother's room was open. He had never been inside since she died. Now he went without a thought to her drawer and pulled out one of her old stockings. This would make an ideal mask. Simple. It would distort his features and probably not be so hot. Inexpensive as well.

Graduation Day found Pete in a coat and tie. His hand played with the stocking in his coat pocket. His fingers massaged the nylon. He listened to the seniors give their good-bye speeches. *Good-bye, Good-bye*, thought Pete. It was sunny so the Principal had set up chairs outside. James sat proudly on the stage. And when he was called forward and handed his diploma he smiled at the audience but singled out Pete in particular. Pete looked up at the sky. There was a moon in a blue sky—Pete had seen it before in the daytime, but he couldn't remember if he was really looking at the moon or its reflection. James began his speech. Pete grudgingly admitted it sounded better than the Principal's. Something about a visionary stance of the world. But he imagined it was only one of many to come, there were nine other students waiting on the stage. He sighed and tried to block it out. He looked back up in the sky. The sun and moon collided. This omen told him nothing new. Survival of the fittest.

MEET MURDER, MY ANGEL

Rupert Adley

the fog had gone so i went to check out whats going
on down on castro i was just hanging out leant up
against this store when this XJS pulls up the electric
window goes down and i reckon ive got a good chance
of scoring cash or dope its all the same this balding
guy say about 40 or 50 sticks his ugly mug out of the
window so i goes over puts my hand on the top of
the car and stares down at him hes got eyes like ive
seen a million times dogs eyes and i know im on to a
winner

what are you into he says
powder pills anything
i think i can manage that—you had crystal before
coke i asks

methedrine he says

not that i know of

well do you wanna get in

sure i says and we drive off to his place stopping off
at his dealers to score this bag of stuff that looks like
rock all white and kinda crunchy yknow anyway we
gets to his place this really neat apartment with speak-
ers all over the joint a little golden birdcage pictures
yknow real tasteful

what dyou do i asks

im a lawyer he shouts from the bathroom

figures i says

hey do you wanna come here and try this

i go to the bathroom mirrors everywhere and i sit on
the edge of the bath hes squatted on the floor and hes
got the needles out this guys wilder than i thought i
reckoned on a quick beat me beat me session boy was
i wrong

whats this stuff like

you had MDA before he asks

sure

well its like that mixed with coke

does it make your dick shrivel up i asks

yeah sometimes—you mind

no not if youre expecting me to get a hardon

well ive got lots of toys i like to play with he says
and he looks up at me like a guilty kid

i bet you have i says

you wanna do this yourself he says offering me a
needle

yeah sure

i straps my arm up and vein hunts—get one first time
and bang up the works in one shot
before i get the spike out it hits me goldrush strong
hot pure he pulls his needle out and looks up at me i
know what he wants and i want to give it to him
i smash him round the face with the back of my fist
and he falls on the floor

can i show you some of my toys sir he scrapes
himself off the ground

yeah but dont stand up stay down on your knees
he crawls through to the bedroom and gets out this
big case from under the bed he empties it on the floor
jeez what a selection dildoes belts boots masks straps
you name it
theres a bag of powder

coke i asks

yes
i undo the bag and tip a pile on the floor i dip my
finger in and it tastes real clean i make a couple of
real big rough lines with my finger and give it the old
vacuum job with a dollar bill i let him have some

what are you going to do to me he says

treat you like a lump of shit you pig fuck i give him
a kick here put this on i says i throw a rubber apron
at him he strips down and puts it on i push him to
the ground put a collar round his neck tie the apron
up and chain up his wrists and ankles i drag him
through to the kitchen pulling him by his collar his
knees mustve skinburnt on the floor cos by the time
ive got him into the kitchen hes leaving blood trails
i pull my dick out and piss on the kitchen floor

are you gonna lick this up or do i have to make you

he doesnt move so i put my boot on the top of his head and push his face splat into the floor

im not playing fucking games i says and he starts licking

dirty pig bastard i says and i go to the bathroom and hits up again shit this stuff is hot i goes back to the kitchen and hes waiting looking up at me

go back to the bedroom i says

i cant he says and hes right hes so trussed up that he can only shuffle along on his knees and chin

oh yeah i asks i go to the drawers and find a big shiny carving knife really heavy and sharp like a razor i turn towards him and hes got this look in his eyes shit scared but like turned on turns me on too i guess

im gonna get changed i says

can you do it in here so i can watch sir

fuck off buttfuck i goes to the bedroom and strips off he was right my dicks shrunk sos i can hardly see it

doesnt look like youre gonna be seeing much action i says and start stripping off shit this stuff is good im flying

i look around at the stuff all over the floor i put on a dirty old pair of biker boots and a massive strap on dildo i keep my leather jacket on and i take this black leather mask with slits for the eyes and a zip for the mouth i pick the knife offa the bed i goes to the bathroom and makes him a syringe i go back to the kitchen needle in one hand mask and knife in the other i get him a good vein stick the spike in and pull the blood out into the syringe

put it in slowly he says i dont like it fast like you
do it take it slow so i shoves it in real fast and he
shouts out its burning i put my boot right up his ass
and he rushes and shuts up real quick i pump it squirt-
ing the blood in hard each time good huh motherfucker hes whining again so i kick him i put the mask
over my head and stand over him

its me whos meant to wear the mask sir he says

shut the fuck up smartass the rules have changed i
show him the knife get into the bedroom go on crawl
you pig bastard he tries this sad attempt shuffling on
his knees and dragging himself by the chin i yanks
him up by the collar and puts the knife in front of
his face shift your fucking ass into the bedroom you
understand the guy is lookin real worried he gets the
feeling im not kidding i drag him into the corridor
and drop him to the ground i kick him over and drops
the knife sos it sticks in the ground near his feet he
struggles away like crazy i pick up the knife and walk
behind him chasing him swinging the knife so if he
slows down i slice it across his butt by the time we
get to the bedroom hes got deep gashes in his ass and
hes sobbing like a baby
i take off his apron and tie him to the bedpost i toot
some more rock and see myself in the mirror like
something from a real bad trip horror movie big black
rubber dick an executioners mask shit was i high

what are you going to do to me he whimpers i walk
over to him and stand with my rubber dick right in
his face he tries to stretch his neck out to suck on the
cock but i pull away and crouch down right in his face

and hold the knife up to his neck hes making little sobbing noises

you love this dontcha i says

no im scared i dont like being this scared

lyin bastard i stares right in his eyes he tries to look away but i hold his face to mine

what are you going to do to me he asks again i lays the knife on the bed and picks up a studded belt i give him an almighty thwak across the face stud side down he cries out it turns me on so i start lashing him like mad big red marks across his fat little body whipping his piggy tits til they bleed he starts moaning whimpering but it sounds different really turned on so i stop

no dont stop please sir dont stop i deserve it sir ive been bad please sir hit me again sir i ram the big rubber dick down his throat

shut up you fuck i says and he hasnt got much choice hes gagging like mad and then he throws up and his puke goes all over my legs ya fucking pig i says and i yank the dick away lick that shit offa my legs and he tries to pull away but i force his face in it and hes gagging and sobbing saying sir sir and hes gone into a kind of trance and he holds onto my legs like a baby and i know that hes mine i kind of love him in a way it may sound dumb but right at that moment i really love him hes mine

kill me he whimpers i know the SM rules and death fantasy stuff but im too far gone by now too far into it why not i think to myself so i pick up the knife and yank his head back the veins on his neck are sticking out and i can feel the blood pumping were both sweating like mad

say that again i says holding the knife against the lump in his throat

kill me please sir please

you mean that

yes please do it please ill be yours forever

i draw my arm back and i drive the heavy blade into his throat blood shoots all over

no he croaks

too late i says and twist the knife and he squirms and its like coming a thousand times

he tries to break out of the restraints with this wheezing noise and he spasms and pisses and shits hisself then goes dead i stick my face in the shower of blood pumping from his neck warm red pumping blood juice spurting out it feels like the ultimate but shit does it feel good im shaking a bit now so i go and take a cold shower and get dressed i take the coke from the bedroom and go to the bathroom to get the crystal i need some spikes so i open the cabinet and theres a thing of lipstick but no needles so i take it and shut the cabinet door there in the mirror is the face of a murderer i twist the lipstick and i smear great wedges of the bright red stuff all over my mouth i go to the bedroom and i give him a kiss a big red lipstick kiss on his dead face and he looks real twisted but jeez does it turn me on i see my face in the mirror and im about to wipe the stuff offa my face but i kinda like it there like a horror movie i goes to walk out and i take one last look at him ill never forget it him trussed up

like the thanksgiving turkey blood all over everywhere
the big old knife sticking outta his neck shit and piss
and rock and puke on the floor and a big lipstick kiss
on his cheek

A TO BEE
(AND BACK AGAIN)

Suzette Partido

IT WAS IN EARLIEST adolescence that I dedicated my small fingers to the worship of older women. Surrounded by down-cheeked nuns throughout primary school, I became adept at the heady game of probing beneath their tailored skirts.

My mind unleashed itself to crawl behind the convent doors. I scooted into cabinets, closets and dresser drawers. What I glimpsed—or thought I glimpsed—was undergarments of mythic proportions. I marveled at what feats of engineering must have been required to hoist oneself into these medical costumes. Girdles and brassieres with straps, buckles and buttons all the color of rye bread. The sweetest feature I gave this intimate finery was an ever-present feminine suggestion of "Lingerie." The most beastly of garments was trimmed with matron lace and pearl-studded bows.

It is true I have always found the wardrobes of older women more alluring, more exotic than that of their daughters or granddaughters. As a child these attractions were instinctual. I was a prepubescent warehouse of unnatural desires. I loved parochial school for its discipline and random beatings. Unlike my girlfriends, I never wanted to be a nun, I only wanted to have one. This desire followed me home each day as I would bullet into the living room and arrange myself for the half-hour rerun of *The Andy Griffith Show*.

I pressed my forehead against the cool glass screen, braving fatal X-ray blindness. I willed the tentacles of my imagination between the rolling lines of the black and white Zenith. I carefully skirted Barney, Andy and Opie and landed in the kitchen of herself, Aunt Bee. For thirty minutes each afternoon I knew what heaven was.

Aunt Bee let me call her Beatrice. She smelt of lilacs and layer upon layer of peach-colored face powder. Throughout the movement of the program, Beatrice and I remained together unless of course she was running food to the feeble men at the courthouse. On such occasions I darted up the stairs to her bedroom and slid ontop her single bed. Waiting for the return of her full attention, I traced the texture of her quilted spread while wishing her full weight pressing down on me, wishing never to leave.

Mostly though, Beatrice and I spent our visits in her kitchen. When someone came home she hid me in her canning pantry until she exchanged the expected pleasantries and sent whomever along their way. Beatrice had no intention of sharing me or explaining me to the others nor had I any desire to leave her domain where the air always seemed to taste of pot roast and cooling pie. This comfort together with her round presence, the warmth of her oven and the bleached features of her kitchen bound into a single female charm I carried with me inside and outside the town of Mayberry. Like feathers and stones tied with string, the essence of Beatrice and her space gave me a belief in the power of all grandmothers and their ancient sexuality. I came to understand the magic workings of housewives and housekeepers.

The lessons Beatrice taught me were not only subtle but infused with the urgency of life and death. Beatrice knew she could never leave the confines of her black and white thirty-minute world. Because of this I knew she would always be there for me. Beatrice displayed her wide vocabulary of tiny facial expressions and their meanings. She taught me to divine unspoken truths found in the space between peoples' words. My lessons came casually over endless cups of tea.

Beatrice would sometimes slip her shoes off and lift her nylon-covered legs onto my lap. As I listened to her stories, I pinched her puffy feet, gently rubbing her bunions and pulling her toes. She often spoke of her troubled youth: awful parents, poverty, bad girls. She sighed to illustrate how she missed the substance of excitement.

When whole shows were devoted to other town members, Beatrice and I carried folding chairs to the backyard. I coaxed her hairpins to the ground and took a brush to her long dust-colored mane. The thrill of her eye-closing smiles pulled me to her pink neck where I left small wet kisses.

There was a day when I knew the end of my life with Beatrice had come. I suppose the actual show was changing stations or viewing times but the real reasons were deeper. Beatrice was keen on the idea that I spend time with girls of my own age. She promised I would find good council in the female form. Her foretelling was a great understatement.

In the twenty years since visiting Beatrice I have refined a taste for older women and their ways of ancient sensuality. I never considered returning to Mayberry an option until now. As a member of the Church of Cable T.V. I dance my thoughts around the midnight showing of *The Andy Griffith Show*. I think perhaps I'll bring her chocolates and roses and wrangle the Sheriff's car for a weekend. I'd like to take Beatrice to a big city hotel, buy her dresses and hats and handbags. We would exercise the rite of roomservice and catch up on my years away and I would finally feel the full weight of her body upon me as she smiled eye-closing smiles.

FRENZY
OF THE FLESH

Stewart Home

STEVE QUEEN disliked the idea of freedom. Had it not been for a deep-seated need to pursue his artistic inclinations, he'd never have left the sleepy village of Burnham in Buckinghamshire. The teenager had enjoyed his strict Methodist upbringing and now that he found himself in a student hostel, he felt lost and alone.

Steve lived for the precious hours he spent in his studio. As long as he was moving a pencil over paper, the youth felt contented. Sometimes after completing a life study, Steve would look at his work and feel repulsed. From childhood, the belief that there was no pleasure to be taken in the nude female form had been instilled in the teenager's mind. Occasionally the art school provided a male model. When that happened Queen felt an unfamiliar stirring in his groin.

The art school Steve was attending, the De Sade, was one of the most prestigious in Britain. Located on London's Gower Street, it was situated between Bloomsbury and Fitzrovia, two of the plusher areas of the capital's West End. On his arrival, Queen had been distressed to discover that many of his fellow students were bohemians. Most found it next to impossible to get up before midday. They'd spend the afternoon nursing coffees in the college cafeteria, while evenings were frittered away drinking in trendy clubs like the Limelight and the Wag. Nights were a time for bonking rather than sleep. Any lulls in this schedule were roughly divided between reading *Viz*, watching tv and doing the odd sketch.

Steve, who got up at five-thirty in the morning to say his prayers, was considered the epitome of squaresville by his fellow students. The Tuesday of Queen's third week at the De Sade seemed no different from any of the other days he'd spent at the college. Steve had taken a break at ten. He'd gone to the cafeteria to get a glass of milk and a buttered roll. As the teenager tucked into his modest fare, John Thomas—a world-famous performance artist who taught in the mixed media department—came and sat beside him.

"Fresher?" Thomas enquired.

"Yes," Steve replied.

"What department are you in?" Thomas demanded.

"Painting," Steve replied.

"You need to be filled with poison," Thomas

announced. "When I've finished my coffee, we'll head over to my studio and start work on it. I get this feeling from you . . . you could be the greatest artist since Van Gogh! But if you're to be anything, you've got to be filled with poison."

"You're the teacher, you know best," Steve's father had beaten respect for authority into his son.

John Thomas has a tried and tested formula for seducing freshers. The first thing he did was make Queen swallow a tab of White Lightning. The acid would take half an hour to hit. In the meantime, Thomas decided to prepare Steve for the performance ritual. This would, of course, be fully documented.

"Take your clothes off," Thomas instructed.

"I can't," Queen replied.

"Why not?" Thomas demanded.

"I'm embarrassed," Steve mumbled.

"Look," Thomas hissed, "if you wanna be a great artist, you'll have to bare your soul to the public. If you're too uptight to take your clothes off in front of me, then you'll never cut it as a genius."

Thomas had a way with words. Before he'd even finished speaking, Queen had begun to unbutton his shirt.

"What's that for?" Steve inquired, pointing at a bath tub full of rotting meat.

"That's for our performance," Thomas explained. "But don't worry about that yet. I'll have to get you prepared first."

When Queen had removed all of his clothing, Thomas took a large jar of Vaseline and began to rub the petroleum jelly onto the fresher's face, hands, genitals and feet and then finally into his arse. Steve had a hard-on throughout the entire operation. After this, Thomas took a roll of gauze and bandaged the youth's face, hands and feet. As his teacher started work on the genitals, Steve's erection was really throbbing. The gauze was wrapped around Steve's balls. Then with expert precision, Thomas wound the bandage around the teenager's straining love muscle. Steve could stand it no longer. He shot off a wad of his genetic dew. The liquid DNA hit the art teacher in the eye, dripped down the side of his face and into his mouth. Thomas was a professional and continued his bandaging as if nothing had happened.

178   At last the preparations were finished, the gauze secured with a safety pin. Thomas removed his own clothing and used the internal telephone system to summon a technical assistant. The technician was wearing a white coat. Steve couldn't see this because a bandage had been wrapped over his eyes. There was a gap in the gauze to allow for the use of his mouth, but otherwise his head and neck were completely covered by the bandage.

The White Lightning was beginning to hit as Thomas maneuvered Steve into the bathtub filled with rotting meat. The youth's mind was filled with a pure white light. It was as if he'd entered heaven. He felt weightless and filled with well-being. Thomas positioned Steve face up in the bathtub and then got in on top of him. He sat so that his shit chute was positioned over Steve's mouth.

Queen began to lick the arsehole. He didn't connect the taste in his mouth with the sweet smell of the sewers. His acid-armed consciousness had convinced him that he was in heaven. Thomas took a Tibetan ceremonial knife and cut into Steve's flesh. The fresher experienced his skin being ripped apart as a sweet carcass. As Queen's tongue lashed into Thomas's arse, the wayward art teacher began to masturbate. Thomas shot off a wad of liquid genetics and then rubbed the DNA into the wounds he'd sliced out of the youth's body.

The art teacher twisted around and shoved his love muscle into Steve's mouth, then picked up a lump of rotting meat and rubbed it all over his body. The fresher sucked his teacher's throbbing member deep into his throat. Queen had retreated to a point beyond consciousness. Although he'd been sexually repressed for every second of his waking life, now that his erotic energies were released, he knew instinctively how to deal with the uncut meat that had been stuffed into his mouth.

Thomas was out on the mudflats. He experienced the smell of rotting meat, wafting up from beneath him, as a salty breeze blown across from a tropical sea. Steve pumped up the volume and Thomas experienced orgasm as a DNA-encoded replay of the first star exploding.

The art teacher flipped Queen around; the fresher's arsehole was well greased and Thomas had no trouble penetrating the sphincter. The top then shoved a piece of rotting meat into Queen's mouth before biting into the student's shoulder. The technician was getting perfect shots on his camcorder.

Thomas was an old hand at the bump and grind routine. But young boys tended to get him overexcited. The art teacher was the wrong side of forty and to be making it with someone still at the peak of physical perfection meant that he was unable to control himself and therefore came earlier than he'd planned. An ego-negating simultaneous orgasm drained the last ounce of energy from the performance art perverts. They had reached that peak from which man and man can never jointly return.

180   Dave Smith was a youth of simple tastes. He didn't ask for much in life. Just a boyfriend who liked getting it eight times a night, a wad of cash in his pocket and the opportunity to spend, spend, spend!

Dave thought art was a load of bullshit. A bourgeois mental set leading to an irrational reverence for activities that suited ruling class needs. Still, his art master at school had considered him a brilliant colorist. An art school career had seemed less hassle to Dave than getting a job. Bunking off college without loss of income was less problematic than skiving off on some underpaid government training scheme. And the money was better too! It was a logical following through of these considerations that led Dave to a degree course at the De Sade.

Dave liked London, it was a damn sight better than the sleepy village he'd left behind in the Cotswolds.

What Smith didn't dig was having to share a room with a religious fanatic who objected to his all-night fuck sessions. Steve Queen was a killjoy. He didn't like partying, hanging out on Old Compton Street or sex. The only things he was into were religion and art—and in Dave's mind there wasn't much difference between them.

Justin Pitt-Simmons was a sadist with a difference. When it came to love relationships, such as the one he was having with Dave Smith, he liked to be beaten up rather than doing the beating. He would only vent his sadistic streak on total strangers—and quite often this meant going to murder and beyond. Justin was a militant antismoker. His victims were always nicotine addicts whom he tortured to death with their own cigarettes.

Justin had been seeing Dave for a week. To date they'd always made love in Justin's shared student room or out in the street. Pitt-Simmons got off on total strangers walking in on his love-making, but with his roommate it had become so commonplace that it was no longer stimulating. Tonight he'd been insistent that he should go back to his boyfriend's room. He'd got his way, and although he'd not met Dave's roommate, he knew the bastard was a religious fanatic. It made him horny just to think about that Jesus freak walking in on them.

Dave was beating out the primitive rhythm of sex. He loved the "scent" of Justin's arsehole. His partner experienced ecstasy as Dave's huge cock penetrated his sphincter. They were no longer in London. The sexual stimulation had activated genetic codings buried deep inside their brains. Their movements were under the Dictatorship of the DNA. Dave and Justin were basking on the mudflats of prehistory.

Steve Queen and John Thomas were midway into another art action. They'd been experimenting with ritual performances for more than a month. The white-coated video technician had recorded all their work for detailed study by posterity. Queen was strung by his feet from the ceiling, his hands were chained to the floor and blood was rushing to his head. In front of him was a video screen. From upside down, he was watching a playback of an earlier action he'd made with John.

182   Thomas was beating out the primitive rhythm of sex. He was holding onto Steve's ankles, his arms stretched out above his head. The art teacher was looking beyond the video screen, into a mirror he'd placed behind it. He studied his reflection as he moved in and out of Steve's arsehole.

Thomas wanted to destroy Steve's sense of identity. The action had reached a crucial stage. During their previous rituals, the youth had been drugged and blindfolded. This was the first time Steve had seen any of his performances played back on video. He was about to discover it wasn't always Thomas who'd fucked him. On a number of occasions, businessmen had paid for the privilege of screwing the teenager.

Thomas beat harder and brought himself to orgasm, simultaneously shooting a wad of liquid genetics into Steve's tight little arsehole. However, the youth didn't register the orgasm. He was mesmerized by the image of a businessman abusing his body—an episode that was being played back on the video screen.

"You're a rent boy," Thomas informed him. "But don't worry, you'll be getting your cut of the loot."

Steve was overcome by a heady mixture of emotions. He screamed. But the youth also had a hard-on and could feel a strange sexual current surging through his body. He'd been used and abused, cheated and lied to. And yet seeing that anonymous prick penetrate his sphincter was a right fucking turn-on.

Steve could feel Thomas's hand on his love muscle, beating the meat. He was barely conscious of the liquid genetics that shot from his prick. Cold thoughts had flooded his brain. Thomas wasn't an artist. It was just a cover for his perverted lusts. Steve felt his innocence had been abused. He knew instinctively that once he was unshackled, he'd take his revenge.

"Don't you feel angry?" Thomas inquired, trying to fathom the teenager's mood.

"Not at all," Steve replied, as a controlled rage enabled him to conceal his very real emotions. "I can see I'm a masochist. I can only thank you for what you've done. You've helped me discover my innermost feelings!"

"In that case," Thomas replied, "I'll unshackle you and we'll go out for a meal to celebrate. I've always wanted my very own sex slave!"

Once Steve was unchained, he leapt at Thomas and pushed him against the end wall of the studio. The white-coated video technician taped every second of

183

the action as Steve beat his teacher's head against the brick wall until there was nothing left of it but a study in blood, pulp and gore.

Once Thomas was dead and his limp body had sunk to the floor, Steve felt a calmness descend upon him. He turned around and looked at the video technician, who was still taping him.

"What are you gonna do with the footage you've shot?" Steve demanded.

"I'll deposit it with my lawyer for safekeeping," the technician replied. "You're a very great artist but this film can't be shown while you're alive. If it was, you'd end up in jail."

"Will you help me avoid punishment for my crime?" Steve asked.

"Once I've stored this and all the other videos safely, I'll come back here and dispose of the body," the video technician announced as he removed a VHS cassette from his camcorder.

"Do you really think I'm a great performance artist?" Steve inquired.

"Of course," the technician replied. "Your teacher was a fake but you're for real."

Steve walked over to the technician and the two men embraced. They kissed passionately and rubbed their crotches together.

"We can't make performance art here," the video technician whispered. "It doesn't seem right."

"We'll meet up in my room," Steve shot back. "If you can just sort out the mess here first."

"No problem," the youth's new performance art partner assured him.

"Got any fags?" Steve wanted to know.

"I didn't know you smoked," the technician replied, hauling three packets of Camel cigarettes from his bag and then handing them to Queen.

The teenager took the smokes and kissed the technician.

"Every genius needs an addictive habit," Steve explained. "Smoking is the least unchristian one I can think of, so I'm taking it up."

The two men embraced again and then parted.

Dave and Justin were doing a sixty-nine when they heard Steve's key in the lock. Justin was really thrilling to the primitive rhythm of sex and as Steve walked into the room, he shot off a wad of liquid genetics. The spunk that Dave managed to avoid swallowing was spilling out of the side of his mouth. But everything was ruined when Justin realized that Queen was puffing on a cigarette. Justin could feel his asthma coming on, and simultaneously a sense of all the injustices he'd suffered welled up inside him. What right did this creep have to spoil his fun? He'd looked forward to the Jesus freak walking in on him as he made love to his boyfriend. But in his wildest dreams, Justin had never imagined the bastard would be a smoker!

Steve lay down on his bed, flicked ash onto the floor. He'd said nothing to Dave and Justin, not even hello. He was lost in his own private thoughts, thinking of the technician whose name he didn't even know — and the art action the two of them were going to make together.

Dave was well aware that Justin had been turned off by the smell of nicotine. He simply wanted to carry on with the sexual athletics but knew this was out of the question until Justin had taken his revenge. He rolled free of Justin, enabling his partner to get up from the bed.

Steve made no effort to resist when Justin hauled him up from his pit. He knew Dave's boyfriend was an art student, so he figured it was all right for the two of them to make some kind of performance action together. Steve didn't even protest when Justin strapped his hands to the light fitting and his legs to the beds that flanked two sides of the room.

Justin ripped Steve's clothes from him. Beneath the thin veil of Steve's Christian morality there was a pagan lust for nude encounters of every kind. A lust that was revealed in Steve's smile and throbbing erection. Justin searched the pockets of the clothes he'd torn from his victim's body and found three packets of Camels—two sealed and one opened. A box of matches completed his haul.

Justin lit a cigarette and stubbed it out on the rim of Steve's arse. His victim squealed in delight. Queen was enjoying this art action. It reminded him of the sessions he'd had with John Thomas.

Justin relit the cigarette, crawled under his victim, then pulled the bastard's mouth open and stubbed the gasper out on Steve's tongue. Justin lit fag after fag, extinguishing them in Queen's ears and mouth and up his nose. As Justin proceeded with the torture session, Steve let out little cries of pleasure. He had not yet caught onto the fact that this was not an art action, that this was for real!

"Your mouth smells like an ashtray!" Justin spat. "You're just a nicotine-addled shitbag, who'd die of lung cancer in a few years if I hadn't decided to put you out of your misery. Your life is nothing compared to the millions of hours your addiction has taken off other people's lives. Passive smokers suffer illness and death through your selfishness. Aren't you ashamed of all the misery you've caused from smoking on trains, buses, in the streets, pubs, shops and lifts? From smoking at other people's homes and smoking when people come to visit you? From smoking at parties and in toilets? Smoking in bed and in motorcars? Worst of all from smoking in cafés, restaurants and at mealtimes in general! Destroying your own tastebuds and everyone else's enjoyment of their food!"

Justin paused, then continued with: "You've not even started suffering yet. I'm gonna teach you the meaning of pain!"

Steve couldn't stifle the beginnings of a giggle.

"What do you think's so funny?" Justin demanded as he stubbed a lighted cigarette on Steve's prick.

"You're going a bit over the top for an art action, aren't you? One that's not even being filmed!"

"Do you think I'm joking?" Justin demanded.

"No," Steve replied. "Art is a serious business. We're making an art action; it's serious, but I think you're hamming it up a bit too much!"

"This isn't a fuckin' art action!" Justin snarled. "I'm gonna kill you!"

Dave put a copy of Iggy and the Stooges' *Raw Power* onto his hi-fi and turned the volume right up. It would drown out any noise the neighbors might find distracting.

Justin lit four smokes, arranged them in his fist and then stubbed the lot into Queen's groin. This time Steve's scream was for real. The pain was much greater now that he knew Justin wasn't indulging him with a display of performance art bravado. This was for real, and reality hurt!

Justin took a lit cigarette and taped the filter to Queen's prick. Steve writhed in agony as the ash burned into his love muscle. He howled but the cries of pain were inaudible over the Stooges' body-odor boogie.

Steve could shake ash off his prick but the fag kept burning down toward the filter, leaving an ever lengthening scar on the sensitive flesh of his genetic pump, while his frantic pleas for mercy did nothing to lessen the agony.

Justin opened his bag and took out a packet of fireworks. He inserted several bangers up Queen's arse, leaving one sticking out, ready to be lit. He put bangers into Steve's ears and up Steve's nose, and a fistful into his victim's mouth.

Queen went stiff with fear. Justin moved with the speed of a striking snake, as the flame from his lighter made contact with firework fuse after firework fuse. From the bangers stuck in Steve's nose to the ones jammed into his mouth, then those in the ears—and finally the one that protruded from Steve's arse.

Justin stepped behind the curtains; Dave had already moved back against the door. As the bangers exploded in Steve's nose and mouth, a sheet of flame shot across the room. Then the fireworks in Queen's ears went off, sending a wave of agony through his brain as his eardrums were blown apart. Steve was dead by the time the shock waves from a final explosion ran up from his arsehole and into his guts, reducing his lower intestines to a bloody pulp.

Justin moved from behind the curtains across to the bed. Dave got on top of the crazed sadist and buggered him to the scorching sound of James Williamson's guitar attack on the Stooges' "Death Trip."

The technician was banging on the door. He got no response although loud music was blasting from the room. The technician tried the handle and the door opened. When he saw Steve's dead and badly mutilated bulk hanging from the light fitting, deep-seated emotions took control of his body. There was an iron lying on the floor. The technician picked it up and smashed it into Dave's skull, killing the art student instantly.

When Dave stopped humping and his body slipped limply from Justin's back, the sadist realized that something was seriously amiss. But the DNA had taken control of his body and his responses were slow. The iron smashed into Justin's head. He was killed by the first blow but the technician kept smashing the blunt instrument into the art student's skull. As he pulped the teenager's brains, the video technician muttered inaudibly that he'd lost his only chance of true love.

The technician could not account for his actions of the previous night. He remembered everything up to seeing Steve's dead body. He knew he'd killed the two guys he'd caught fucking in Steve's room. The blokes he'd done in must have murdered his teenage piece. After that the technician walked aimlessly for hours. Then he'd got hold of some booze. He'd a hell of a hangover when he woke up.

Worries about the hospital appointment had nagged at the back of the technician's brain for weeks. If it hadn't been for his alcohol-induced stupor, he'd have arrived early for the consultation, not late. He'd wanted the results, if only to know the worst. That's what he'd said to the doctor, tell me the worst. And he's got a straight reply:

"I won't lie to you," the doctor said, "the cancer has spread from your lungs and into your bones. There's nothing we can do. Personally, I'd give you a month to live at the most."

"What did I do to deserve this?" the technician wailed.

"By your own admission, you've smoked forty cigarettes a day for the past fifteen years," the doctor replied sternly. "You have only yourself to blame for your condition."

MO' BETTER MALCOLM

Darius James

OPEN ON:
ART CARD MODELLED AFTER THE 1930S'
POSTER FOR THE JAMES WHALE CLASSIC
FRANKENSTEIN, FEATURING A NECK-
BOLTED FIGURE OF MALCOLM X ESCAPING
A MOB OF ANGRY, TORCH-BEARING BUPP-
IES IN ARMANI SUITS, WHICH READS: He's
badd! He's *black!!* He's *back from the dead!!* He's—

"Mo' Better Malcolm"
('Cuz I need Mo' Better 'Magination Fo' Mo' Better
Title)
"Another Rock-Packed Spike Lee Pipe!!!"
ON THE LOWER-LEFT CORNER OF THE
ART CARD, THERE IS AN OVAL OF **SPIKE LEE**

WITH A GLASS CRACK-PIPE HANGING
FROM THE SIDE OF HIS MOUTH. THE
SMOKE CLOUD OF HIS DIALOGUE BAL-
LOON READS:

> SPIKE LEE
> That's right, folks! *I'm buggin' an'*
> *on the pipe!* With the money I make
> off you suckas on this "joint," I'm
> gonna buy *Peru!*

DISSOLVE TO:

EXT. GRAVEYARD—NIGHT

A BAT FLAPS ACROSS THE CRESCENT OF A
WANING MOON. THE SHADOWS OF TWO
FIGURES ARE CAST AGAINST A ROW OF
ERODING HEADSTONES. THE HEAD-
STONES READ:

Marcus Garvey	W. E. B. Dubois
George Jackson	Bob Marley.
Patrice Lumumba	Franz Fanon
Huey P. Newton	General China

THE SHORTER OF THE TWO, **DR. SPIK-
ENSTEIN**, PORTRAYED BY SPIKE LEE,
WHOSE KNOB-KNEED, TOOTHPICK-THIN
LEGS SPROUT FROM A PAIR OF AFRICAN-
PRINT BERMUDA SHORTS, CARRIES AN
ANTIQUE OIL LAMP IN HIS FIST. HE WEARS
A PAIR OF UNLACED "AIR JORDAN" SNEAK-
ERS ON HIS FEET AND A BASEBALL CAP
WITH AN "X IN CIRCLE" LOGO READING

"Mo' Better Malcolm" ON HIS HEAD. IN BOLD DISNEYESQUE LETTERING, HIS T-SHIRT READS **"PIG TALES."** UNDERNEATH IS A DRAWING, AFTER CARTOONIST CARL BARKS, OF UNCLE SCROOGE McDUCK WITH SPIKE LEE'S HEAD: *"Starring Uncle Spike McDuck."* UNCLE SPIKE McDUCK SWIMS IN A MOUNTAIN OF GOLD COINS. UNDERNEATH THE DRAWING, THE T-SHIRT READS: *"A Spike Lee Joint for the Kiddies."*

THE SECOND FIGURE, **REV. AL**, PORTRAYED BY REV. AL SHARPTON, IS A FAT, HUMPBACKED, ONE-EYED TROLL WITH A PROCESSED POMPADOUR WRAPPED IN DOO-RAG. HE CARRIES A SATCHEL FILLED WITH SHOVELS AND PICKAXES OVER HIS LEFT SHOULDER. THE BUTTON PINNED TO HIS DOO-RAG READS:

"Tawana Told The Truth, *Ruth!*"
DR. SPIKENSTEIN'S LANTERN CASTS A CIRCLE OF LIGHT ON A SMALL, OBLONG BRASS PLATE ATTACHED TO A HEADSTONE. THEY STOOP TO READ:
El-Hajj Malik El-Shabazz
May 19, 1925 – February 21, 1965

REV. AL SHARPTON
We've arrived, Master. It's brother Malcolm!

DR. SPIKENSTEIN SLAPS REV. AL ACROSS
THE HUMP WITH HIS BALLCAP.

DR. SPIKENSTEIN
I can see that, *hankahead!* I didn't lose my
eye beggin' som' pussy offa crazy "Colt 45"
ho'!

DISSOLVE TO:
MONTAGE OF REV. AL'S HEAD IN FISH-EYE
CLOSE-UP. THIS SEQUENCE IS IN BLACK
AND WHITE. REV. AL TALKS DIRECTLY
INTO THE CAMERA'S LENS. DETAIL SWEAT,
FLARING NOSTRILS WITH MUCUS-CAKED
NOSE HAIR. BLOODSHOT EYES, SALIVA
SWARMING WITH FLIES, ETC.

REV. AL
OH BABY! PLEASE BABY! PLEASE PLEASE
BABY!

THE FINAL SHOT OF REV. AL SHOWS A
JAGGED COKE BOTTLE GOUGING OUT HIS
EYE. BLOOD AND QUIVERING EYEJELLY
SPURTS FROM ITS SOCKET.

REV. AL
OW-OW BABY! OW!!!

DISSOLVE TO:
AS HE ADJUSTS HIS BALLCAP, DR. SPIK-
ENSTEIN CONTINUES TO VERBALLY ABUSE
THE HUMPBACKED REV AL.

DR. SPIKENSTEIN
And stop draggin' your knuckles
on the ground like the Gorilla

194

you look like! Stand up! Walk
proud like a natural Nubian Man!
Now start digging!

FADE UP
EXT. WINDMILL—NIGHT
HEAVY RAIN POURS FROM THE SKY. THE
WIND BLOWS WITH FURY. A BOLT OF
LIGHTNING STRIKES A BOX KITE FLYING
FROM THE WINDMILL'S ROOF.

CUT TO:
INT. "FORTY ACRES AND A MULE" LABORA-
TORY—NIGHT
SPARKS OF ELECTRICITY SPIT FROM A
GRAFENBERG GENERATOR IN THE "FORTY
ACRES AND A MULE" LABORATORY, IGNIT-
ING THE HEAD AND NECK BOLTS OF MAL-
COLM X'S CORPSE LYING ON AN
OPERATING TABLE. MALCOLM'S HAND
SUDDENLY TREMBLES TO LIFE.
    DR. SPIKENSTEIN IS IN A PAROXYSM OF
ECSTASY.
                DR. SPIKENSTEIN
HE'S ALIVE! HE'S ALIVE! NOW I KNOW
WHAT IT FEELS TO BE LIKE ALLAH! *OR IS IT
JAH?*

MALCOLM X SITS UP ON THE OPERATING
TABLE, LOOKS AROUND. CUT TO:
MALCOLM'S P.O.V.—"THE FORTY ACRES
AND A MULE" LABORATORY LOOKS LIKE A

195

CROSS BETWEEN THE ORIGINAL 1930S SET FOR DR. FRANKENSTEIN'S LABORATORY AND THE INTERIOR OF "SPIKE'S JOINT" ON DEKALB AVENUE IN BROOKLYN. IT IS GLUTTED WITH T-SHIRTS, BASEBALL CAPS, VIDEOCASSETTES, TRADE PAPERBACKS AND MOVIE POSTERS. FRUIT OF ISLAM THUGS STAND GUARD AT THE EXITS, SNACKING ON CARROT CAKE.

THE MALCOLM MONSTER IS DISGUSTED. CLEARLY, HE DOESN'T LIKE THIS "JOINT" ONE BIT. HE BOLTS FROM THE OPERATING TABLE AND BARRELS TOWARD THE EXIT. HE IS RESTRAINED BY THE FRUIT OF ISLAM THUGS.

DR. SPIKENSTEIN WALKS OVER TO THE MALCOLM MONSTER, HANGING A WALL CLOCK AT THE END OF A GOLD CHAIN AROUND HIS NECK. A SPINNING-ARMED CARICATURE OF SPIKE LEE'S "MARS BLACK-MON" CHARACTER IS PAINTED ON THE CLOCK'S NUMBERED FACE.

> DR. SPIKENSTEIN
> *Yo! Hold up!* We gotta pull your
> coat to the *new agenda* before you
> go out and set the world on fire
> as Spike Lee's new and improved—
> *Mo' Better Malcolm!*

DISSOLVE TO:

EXT. MECCA—DAY

WITH THE TINY SPARKS OF AN LSD HAL-
LUCINATION FLOATING BEFORE THEIR
EYES, MALCOLM X AND JIMI HENDRIX
CRUISE PASS A MOSQUE IN THE COMPANY
OF TWO WHITE, FRIZZY-HAIRED, PEASANT-
BLOUSED HIPPIE WOMEN WITH BIG BUSTS.

      HIPPIE TEENIE BOP (TO MALCOLM)
        . . . as the plaster hardens, it gets
      really hot, and you start to leak . . .

3 OVALS OF MALCOLM, DR. SPIKENSTEIN
AND REV. AL ARE SEEN IN VARIOUS COR-
NERS OF THE FRAME. MALCOLM'S OVAL
SHOWS HIS SHOCK AND DISGUST. HIS
HAND RESTS NEAR A HUGE ELECTRICAL
WALL SWITCH.

      DR. SPIKENSTEIN (IN OVAL)

You been dead a long time, brother! We don't play
that "vow of poverty" shit no mo'! This is the
nineties! Our leader's got to keep some money in
they pockets! Back in the sixties, it was "propaganda
by deed," but you were long dead before things got
going really good!

      REV. AL (IN OVAL)

Yeah, brother! You missed out on Hendrix, a lot
of good acid, and bonin' young white girls in
the mud at Woodstock!

ON DR. SPIKENSTEIN

DR. SPIKENSTEIN

Nowadays, we market our shit. Package it like it was an Aunt Jemima waffle! Drop it in a toaster, *instant revolution!* No muss! No fuss! We put our revolution on television, throw it up on the movie screen, put a drum machine behind it and then press it on wax! We even got it on a pair of jogging shorts! Today, we say *Market the Revolution or Not at All*, dig?

Just picture it, Malcolm, I'll make you more famous than Mickey Mouse! *And think of the subsidiary rights!* We'll present a revolutionary new line of hair care products—

FADE TO:
BOTTLES OF SHAMPOOS AND HAIR CONDI-TIONERS WITH MALCOLM X'S PICTURE ON THE LABEL. ONE BOTTLE READS: "Malcolm X Jheri Curls."

DR SPIKENSTEIN (IN OVAL)
Malcolm X For Your Natural: *For those who really need to get their head together!*

FADE TO:
CORNUCOPIA OF MALCOLM X MERCHAN-DISE. SKIN LIGHTENERS, WRISTWATCHES, KITES, BURGER KING DRINKING CUPS, MICROWAVED FOOD PRODUCTS, ETC.

DR. SPIKENSTEIN (IN OVAL)
We'll put your face on lunchboxes and bubble gum cards! Or how about a Malcolm X Breakfast Cereal? We'll wipe Cap'n Crunch right off the shelves!

CUT TO:
INT. KITCHEN—MORNING
MALCOLM X SITS AT THE DINING TABLE WITH "THE SIMPSONS," EATING THE NEW MALCOLM X BREAKFAST CEREAL.

DR. SPIKENSTEIN (IN OVAL)
We'll strike a deal for a Saturday Morning Cartoon Show–"Malcolm X Comes to Your House," dig it? Each week, you'll reform a family of white racists, or teach a crackhead the true meaning of black pride, produced with your wacky but profound sense of humor!

ON BART SIMPSON WEARING A "BLACK BART" T-SHIRT.

BART SIMPSON
Black and brown germs?!! Yacoub?!!
Jeeziz, Malcolm, lighten up! Suck in
your lips (h'yuck! h'yuck!)

CUT TO:
MALCOLM X 'ACTION FIGURE' HOLDING HANDS WITH BARBIE DOLL IN BARBIE'S MALIBU "DREAM HOUSE."

DR. SPIKENSTEIN (IN OVAL)
And we'll do product tie-ins with Malcolm X Action

Figures! Who knows? You could end up as Barbie's
new dream date!

DISSOLVE TO:

BARBIE DOLL
Oh, Malcolm! My Original Man! I'm
so proud to be your Nubian Queen!

DISSOLVE TO:
FORTY ACRES AND A MULE LABORATORY.
DR. SPIKENSTEIN HOLDS OUT HIS PALM IN
A GREASY "MO' BETTER BLUES" POSE.

DR. SPIKENSTEIN
If you join the "Forty Acres and a Mule" team, and
play ball with us, we'll get you some new sneakers!
"Air Jordans!"
We got plenty of ballcaps, brother! What do you say?
You down with the program?

MALCOLM X RECOILS FROM SPIKE'S REPUL-
SIVE POSE, HIS HAND FALLING ON THE
ELECTRICAL WALL SWITCH. DR. SPIK-
ENSTEIN BREAKS INTO A SWEAT, HOLDING
UP HIS HANDS IN CAUTION.

DR. SPIKENSTEIN
DON'T TOUCH THAT SWITCH!
MALCOLM'S FACE LIGHTS UP IN REALI-
ZATION.

DR. SPIKENSTEIN
We can work this out, good brother! Let's talk
about this over lunch. *Waiter!*

A FRUIT OF ISLAM WAITER ROLLS OUT A
BUFFET CART PILED HIGH WITH BEAN
PIES. DR. SPIKENSTEIN TALKS BETWEEN
MOUTHFULS OF PIE.

DR. SPIKENSTEIN
Let's see, hmmm. Now, I know you don't be doin'
no kinda nasty when you be dead an' shit. And I
seriously doubt Betty want to be goin' down on
some moldy, dead for twenty-seven years dick!
Somehow, I can't imagine her gettin' all wet an'
freakish behind swallowing a gob of jism squirming
with maggots. But there is one *skeezer* who would.

DR. SPIKENSTEIN TWIRLS HIS HANDS
WITH A DRAMATIC FLOURISH, FARTS AND   201
PRESENTS **THE BRIDE OF DR. SPIK-
ENSTEIN**, PORTRAYED BY JOIE LEE. WITH
A WILD SHOCK OF HENNA HAIR SPRAYING
STRAIGHT INTO THE AIR, SHE ENTERS THE
LABORATORY WRAPPED IN A TIGHT EVE-
NING GOWN MADE UP OF GAUZY WHITE
STRIPS, LOOKING EXACTLY LIKE THE
NINETEEN-YEAR-OLD ELSA LANCHESTER,
ONLY DARKER.

DR. SPIKENSTEIN
(LEERING WITH PRIDE)
She like to rumpty bumpty
like Humpty Dumpty. I know.
I built her myself!

ON THE TWIN REFLECTIONS OF MAL-

COLM'S "BRIDE" IN HIS EYES. UP BILL LEE
JAZZ SCORE.

> DR. SPIKENSTEIN (O.S)
> *Divine*, isn't she?

PULL BACK TO HEAD SHOT. MALCOLM'S
MOUTH GAPES OPEN IN HORROR. HE FIN-
GERS THE WALL SWITCH AS HE SPEAKS.

> MALCOLM X
> *Pretender to Yacoub*—with head the size of
> my rotted testicle! No one "divine"! You are
> like the maggots who feed on my flesh! You
> celebrate the stinking body of the dead!

202

> DR. SPIKENSTEIN
> —But Brother Malcolm! I'm the Original No-
> Pork, Elijah Muhammed "Eat to Live! Live to
> Eat," Bean Pie and Carrot Cake, Fish-an'-
> Chicken-Eatin' Vegetarian Nubian Man! Here,
> have some bean pie. Let's discuss this . . .

MALCOLM SLAPS THE PIE TO THE FLOOR.

> MALCOLM X
> Maggot-man, you belong dead like me! Besides,
> bean pie makes me fart!

MALCOLM PULLS THE SWITCH.

EXT. WINDMILL—NIGHT
THE WINDMILL EXPLODES. BOOM! A PILE
OF RUBBLE.

SCREEN GOES TO BLACK. THE FOLLOWING
EPIGRAPH APPEARS IN WHITE LETTERS:

"I guess it would be impossible for anyone ever to
realize fully how complete my belief in Elijah Muham-
mad. I believed in him not only as a leader in the
ordinary human sense, but also I believed in him as a
divine leader . . . [it is] very dangerous for people to
hold any human being in such esteem, especially
to consider anyone some sort of 'divinely guided' and
'protected' person."—Malcolm X

INDULGENCES

Gil Cuadros

MY MOTHER AND FATHER had both come from the same hometown, Merced, California, romanticized the red checkerboard-patterned water tower on J Street, the Purina feed store on K, the old, semidemolished church that looked of Mexico, rough-hewn, gritty pink stone, L Street. Pulling off the highway, my parents would cluck their tongues, stare out of our black Impala, disbelieving the changes. They told my brother and me of the time when blacks had kept to their own side of town. "Now the place has gone to pot."

Dad parked at the small grocery store, El Mercado Merced, a converted house, boarded-up windows, wrought-iron bars for protection. The place had a little bit of everything: dark, warped wooden shelves carrying sodas, tortillas, lard and eggs, things the neighbors always seemed to run out of first. It was central to both sides of my family. Uncle Rubén lived near the corner; Grandma Lupe across the street; Uncle Cosme, next to her. My great-grandfather Tomás had lived two houses down. "Papa" would walk this street every day, wave at my relatives as he passed by, his cane steadying his balance. It was Rubén who went to try to see in the windows why Papa hadn't gone by that day. It was Cosme who called two days ago to tell us Papa was dead.

My little brother and I ached out of the car, the long ride having caused our legs to fall asleep. Jess had kept on complaining the whole way that I was invading his side, my father turning from his steering: "Do I have to remind you that you are fourteen years old and should just ignore your younger brother?" Dad was already irritated and said he was going to take Jess to Grandma Lupe's. I was to go with my mother. My mother wanted me to mind because some-one had died.

"It's out of respect," she warned while she collected the things she needed from the glove box: a mirror, makeup, tissue. And as we walked the short distance down the street, I looked back and saw my father pull out a six-pack of beer from the old cooler in front of the *mercado*. His hands dripped melted crushed ice, and the sidewalk had become stained with its moisture.

My great-grandfather's house had always reminded me of a ranch, the oppressive heat of the San Joaquin Valley, the large wagon wheel leaning against the standing mailbox, the way the long, tan stucco build-ing hugged the ground. I expected tumbleweeds to roll by, a rattlesnake to be coiled seductively in the flowerbed's rocks. My mother's cousin, Evelyn, had been taking care of Papa and she met us at the door before we even knocked. My mother had just straight-

206

ened herself again, licking the tips of her fingers in the driveway, touching up her hair on the porch. Evelyn and my mother fell into each other's arms as soon as they saw each other, making a show of tears, almost religiously. She was the same age as my mother, thirty, a few months apart. I stood awkward on the porch, afraid to walk in unannounced. Evelyn wore a flimsy dress, a brownish print the same color as the house. Her teeth were stained, and when she smiled her long dogteeth poked out. Hair hung down her back like dry weeds.

"Well," she said, facing me, "who is this foxy young man?"

My mother laughed. "This is my oldest boy." Evelyn swung her dress like she was dancing to a *ranchero* tune, showing her kneecaps, and I stared. My mother always wore pants and it was strange, I thought, for a woman to be home in a dress. She wasn't going anywhere.

She tilted her head coyly at me. "Why don't you give me a big hug. We're family." I put my arms around her like a mechanical claw. She pulled me in tight, placing my face above her breast. I could smell her sweat, a scent of dairy products, cheese and bad milk. It felt like her breast had dampened my face and I wiped away droplets from my cheek. "He looks like your old man, Lorraine." My mother acknowledged, stood near a cabinet filled with ceramic salt and pepper shakers, ashtrays from Vegas, Tahoe, and the biggest little city, Reno. Mom had confided to me she wanted something to remember Papa by.

My mother said, "I just came over, Evelyn, to see where it happened." She held a ceramic Siamese cat, an ear broken off, holes bored in its head.

Evelyn explained that she had come home late from work, she had found him in the bathroom, collapsed, a green mess pooled underneath him. She said, "He started having trouble, not making it in time, then I'd have to clean it up. Sometimes he'd lose it just sleeping in his chair. I told your mother, Lorraine, that he should go into a home. No one wanted to hear about it. I couldn't take care of him twenty-four hours a day."

My mother started to cry again and walked over to see the bathroom, a tissue covering her nose and mouth. I stood with Evelyn. I had heard so many stories about her, how she was dropped from the crib, how soft and impressionable the skull is at that age. My aunts would start low and sympathetic, how it wasn't Evelyn's fault for the way it was with her, but then tell each other what a tramp, a slut Evelyn had become. They'd snicker about how she slept with black men, white men. Papa should have put her away. Evelyn's Papa's angel. Evelyn's a lesbian.

Evelyn smiled at me. I looked around the living room, touched the lamps made out of thick coiled ropes, burlap shades. Evelyn lit a cigarette, clicked shut the silver-toned Zippo lighter. "Do you have a girlfriend?"

"No, not really," I answered.

I felt embarrassed, my whole family was always asking when was I going to get a girlfriend. My mother begged me to find a girl soon, not to be so shy, that it was natural for me to like girls. She'd say she worries because she's a mother, don't you want to make your father proud, your brother should look up to you. The truth was I had a lot of friends who were girls. They would pass notes with me in class, short lined confessions of love for some other boy. Their reasons for love were always the same; the color of eyes, the length of hair, the muscles sneaking out from the boys' short-sleeved shirts. These same boys would shove me around before the bus, their hands on my chest, my shoulders. My body would grow warm, my heart would pound. I would notice the color of their eyes, the strength they possessed. "Fucking sissy," they would say and then one good last punch.

Evelyn seemed like she couldn't believe I wouldn't have a girlfriend. "Oh, then you like someone, what's her name?" I squirmed that I didn't like anyone and they didn't like me. She offered me a sip of her soda, it fizzed in a glass, water had ringed on the wood coffee table.

"No, thank you," I said.

"Oooh, you're so polite. Why don't you sit next to me." I came over to the afghan-covered couch where she sat. I could hear my mother's sobs, the bathroom becoming an echo chamber. Evelyn moved close to me on the couch. "I bet you kiss like a stud," she said. She put her hand on my knee and I started to feel a horrible warmth between my legs, growing. She squeezed my thigh as if to make me laugh, then asked, "What do you do for fun?"

I stumbled as I stood up, fell back down. "I go to

the Scouts," I offered, hoping the conversation would end and my mother would reenter the scene, grab me by the wrist and take me away.

Evelyn looked deep in my eyes, as if to devour a creamy pastry. "Will you do me a favor?" she asked. I nodded, hoping it would involve leaving. "Will you kiss me?" I pulled back but she came forward and vise-gripped my head. Her other hand reached down and grabbed onto my dick, her nails digging into the khaki material of my pants. I wanted to vomit, her breath was like my father's, unclean, like a whole night of beer. I shoved her hand off my lap and got up. I licked the sleeve of my shirt, trying to get the taste of her out. She started to laugh as I unlocked the door.

The brightness of outside kicked in my allergies and I started to sneeze as I ran to Grandma Lupe's house, saying out loud, "Forget my mother." My father sat on the steps drinking his Miller's, tried to grab onto my butt as I passed him. I let the screen door slam behind me and ran for the nearest bathroom, Grandma Lupe's. I barely made it before I puked. From inside I could hear my Grandma talking on the phone saying Evelyn should have been locked up a long time ago. My head hung over the tub's edge, water rushing down the drain. The porcelain reeked of Calgon and Efferdent.

Tension and humidity hung in the old house. Relatives were arriving every moment, my grandmother wringing her hands. My mother was still crying that she couldn't depend on anyone; my brother, too young; my father, always drinking; and me, worthless. I was too embarrassed to tell her why I had run out of Evelyn's and had decided to hide out in the backyard. I was surprised that my mother had come to get me. My brother and I were playing in the old leaning garage, an ancient Chevy on blocks, barrels of pecans and walnuts at the far end, the back entrance to the chicken coop.

My mother wanted me at the kitchen table with all my aunts and my mother's aunts. I was the only guy except for two *viejos*, my mother's uncles, both too old to decline the meeting. My mother said, "You are family. You need to hear."

My Grandmother Mikala sat at the center of the long kitchen table, mirrored the Last Supper needle-point that hung, framed, above her head. Grandma Mickey's face was near silhouette because of the big open windows behind her. Jars of *nopales* glittered in the pantry. Cactus grew along the fence outside and guarded this secret meeting. Just as my mother would light up at the onset of a long story, Mickey smoked a Newport. "As you know, I went to the police. Papa had horrible bruises on his body, especially on his hand, like someone had kept on slamming the door on his wrist. I think Evelyn killed him, made him have a heart attack. The bruises were ugly on his hand."

Around the table, aunts and cousins shook their heads, each taking turns. "Evelyn has always been crazy. She was spoiled rotten by Papa. He never saw how evil she was. He always gave her dresses and toys, didn't give anything to us kids."

Grandma Mickey raised her open palms. "I will make her pay, I swear." I felt sickened that a murderess kissed me that day and I wanted to interrupt Mickey, to tell her Evelyn kissed me and grabbed between my legs. Mom made me put my hand down, kept it hidden below the table, squeezing the fingers occasionally.

My mother's Uncle Rubén spoke. "It's all our own faults, we should have never left him alone with her. Mikala, you should have taken him instead of leaving him with that crazy prostitute. And where is Evelyn's mother? Mary is always gone, never responsible. *Ijo!* It was bad enough Papa had to take Evelyn in and raise her, just because Mary didn't want her child in an institution."

Mikala again raised her palms. "It would kill Mary to know her own girl killed Papa." There was argument all around the table on what to do, then dinner was passed, refried beans, peppered steak, homemade tortillas, Pepsi taken out dusty from the cellar. We all ate with gusto, ready to stone Evelyn, and I held my secret, knowing it wasn't important. All around me people were saying, "Eat, Gilberto, eat."

I had never been to a wake before, the orange and purple summer night having just started, the air extremely dry. I could make out bats flying against the sunset. My Grandma Mickey and all her sisters were behind dark netting, a special section for the immediate family. From behind the curtain, I could hear their sobbing. My mother whispered to my father that

Evelyn was inside and it wasn't fair, none of the other cousins were there. My father sighed, uninterested. I pretended to be appropriately mournful since I'd never seen a dead body before. It lay in its open coffin, a spotlight illuminating his pasty face like a stage actor, I thought. My mother huffed, "It makes me sick, you can hear her going on and on."

My father said, hot-tempered, "She has a right to her grief."

My mother turned into quick anger. "You know what I mean, Danny, you heard what my mother said."

Exasperated, my father whispered sideways, "You have no proof."

"The bruises, Danny, the bruises," my mother near spat till my father said, "Shh!" In the quiet before the wake, I could easily make out Evelyn's wails. They were the kind of wails that could be mistaken as laughing, as if this were all a joke and my great-grandfather would pop up then yell, "We pulled a fast one on all of you!"

I thumbed through the small book given to me as I had entered the mortuary. *How to say the Rosary Apostolic and Other Indulgences.* Grandma Mickey said it was a gift for me, "the mysteries were great and powerful for the devout, the joyful, sorrowful and glorious acts of Jesus purify our sins." It was pretty boring stuff, fifteen Our Fathers and one hundred and fifty Hail Marys. The pictures made it seem more exciting.

After the wake, uncles, aunts, grandparents and children waited on the steps of the mortuary, leaning against the colonnades. An aunt kicked a strip of no-slip on a step with the point of her shoe, her husband held his jacket over his arm, his short-sleeved shirt exposing the various tattoos of roses and crosses. Another man spoke with him, a full black mustache covered his mouth's expression. Aunt Mary had been hastily escorted out by her youngest daughter. Evelyn stood by the coffin long after everyone left. "Nearly threw herself on top," an uncle said. Everyone had moved their cars so they blocked all the exits, the headlights aimed for the front door, the marble walls, the angels and muscular men along the frieze. Rubén called out, "She's coming."

When Evelyn walked outside all the car lights turned on their high beams, people walked away from the shadows, their hiding spots. They began yelling, "Get out of here! We know you did it. You murdered Papa. Sick, sick, sick!" Evelyn had been covering her eyes, trying to see, to adjust. She wore an open black crochet top and the headlights bore through to flesh, bounced off the black Qiana dress as if made of white.

She started to scream, to reason, "I didn't do it." I wondered why she just didn't run or why one of my uncles didn't put a stop to this, their barrel chests filled with breath, their shirts almost too tight, the top button aching to pop. But they wouldn't. She tried to block her eyes with her hands, shaking her head. "He always shitted on himself." Horns blared, hands heavy on steering wheels, my brother leaned on ours from the backseat, our father having rushed us in early. My Grandmother Mikala walked up to Evelyn and began to slap her, nails curled to puncture, looking fierce.

Evelyn defended herself, thrust herself like a cat, wild and rare, on top of my grandmother, both falling dangerously down the steps, backs, spines, shoulder blades hitting the corners. People rushed in like a mob, women pulling on her hair, kicking Evelyn in the stomach, the ass, her breast. The men tried, some laughing, to extract their wives from the brawl. My brother and I jumped up and down in the backseat, acted as if we could feel the blows or were giving them, vocalized the sound of each good hit, "uhh, opff." We watched as Dad returned with my mother, nearly scratching his eyes out, her saying loudly, "That bitch."

My father hastily drove away to his mother's house, it now fully night. My mother told me to forget what had happened, that it wasn't a good thing, that she was already feeling ashamed, her voice quiet and firm. She thought that maybe I should pray, my little brother asleep already, his straight black hair next to my thigh. I rolled the window down slightly, letting the air rush in. I could barely hear the radio, a scatter of signals. I stared outside, wondered if my family would ever turn on me, where would I go, who would I love. The long farm roads leading back greeted my thoughts, the rows of grapevines, tomato furrows, cotton, all lined up in parallel paths ending on the horizon, designed like manifest destiny. Lit by my father's high beams, still ignited, I watched as we passed a scarecrow off the road, dry weeds for hair, a flimsy brown dress, a stake skewered up through the body, arms stretched open as if to embrace.

SAIDA

Rikki Ducornet

I RECALL THAT on the professor's desk, a scarlet beetle levitated upon its pin. And that as he scolded his daughter, Saida, I fixed the beetle with my eyes so as not to give myself away for a coward and a fool by weeping or laughing.

Her crime was this: she had seized me by the wrist and together we had trespassed within the confines of her father's study. Here Saida revealed a terrible mystery: a two-headed cobra, taken in Luxor, and bottled.

Saida had placed the snake on a small table in full sunlight in order to impress me and so master my heart. Although my heart was already hers; only an hour before, in a chamber as cluttered as a tomb, and as I lay napping beside her in a bed cocooned with mosquito netting, she had touched me with candor and fire, pressed her mouth to mine, taken my tongue between her teeth—so that I fell at once into a species of swoon, the bed spinning in a fiery orbit. For hours we breathed a turbulent air.

The air within the professor's forbidden room was turbulent, too, and the snake was hot: it glowed in its keeping medium like a glass wand in a kiln.

Much of Saida's mystery had evolved from conversations shared throughout her unique childhood with her father. She knew of a tribe beyond Egypt's southmost border which included in its totemic system the boiled bones of meat, sexual passion and the color blue. These people tattooed their faces and the backs of their hands with blue zoological series; the tattoos were simultaneously prestigious and magical.

These things I had learned from Saida the very first time we spoke together in the school gardens, after she had teased me for wearing a Koran as a charm, prodding it disdainfully. It dangled between a teapot the size of a thumbtack and with an articulated lid, and a tiny Turk's slipper. I told her the bracelet had belonged to my mother.

My father was a missionary, and I had been nurtured with the poisoned milk of his own thwarted desires. Malevolence, in Father's fevered view, was ubiquitous, yet lacked specific definition, so that the world was jinxed by a multiplicity of prohibitions and temptations; everything of intensity—pleasure and pain, beauty and ugliness, the bitter and the sweet—seduced me equally.

The instant Saida's knowing finger touched me, the room, at once diurnal and nocturnal, and reflecting us as might a necromancer's mirror of molten lead, had itself become so hot it is a wonder our shoes, abandoned on the floor, did not burst into flame—

As had the shoes of a classmate whose home had caught fire; her shoes had saved her. Awakening to the sound of them hissing on the roasting floor, she had screamed.

Until Egypt, my knowledge of fire was academic. Those shoes transmuting to ash upon the floor, and my soul burning in Saida's embrace, revealed fissures reaching into the world's wild center—as would her father's treasures, yet unseen, cooking in the shadows.

I have said that Saida had placed the canopic bottle on a small table, the better to see it. If, as we gazed upon it, Saida had not embraced me, nothing would have happened. But she reached out suddenly and clasped me, and we fell together, knocking the little table over. As the table disclosed four claws and four brass balls, the snake tumbled from its shattered glass. A fine old book titled *Coleoptera of the Sahara* fell also. Sopping up the keeping medium, its green leather binding veered to pink. The rug, too, was discolored by the snake's bathwater.

Later that night, alone in a room furnished only with a bed and a Bible, I remember thinking that Saida and I were like the snake: two-headed and joined as a woman and a man (and it was Saida who had informed me of this joining). Our fictive fucking was as potent as a life-giving venom, an intoxication.

Only because Saida's father was such a distinguished figure did mine allow those weekly visits. The professor's study roiled with a multitude of queerly beautiful things, and my father had warned me that the contemplation of nature was evil. God's world was not to be scrutinized. It contained, by a cosmic error he could not explain, or would not, a pervasive evil.

In other words, if one looked too closely at a thing, one risked finding oneself eye to eye with the Prince of Darkness. As when looking too long at one's reflection one might see something hellish within one's own face: large doses of a smooth mirror could reveal the soul's features. (Navigated in a silence suggesting illness, our house was mirrorless. It contained no treasure or luxury.)

And if Saida's love had revealed a fracture of another sort, a precipice of which I had no previous knowledge, the fire that had reduced the hotel to a black smear had revealed a fracture in the earth and the mummified body of a girl, her bandages seeded with symbols of potencies: little clay figures glazed blue.

The professor scolded his daughter, all the while looking at me. And because I continued to stare at the beetle—pinned through the scutellum and swimming in air—having chosen that point in space as a mooring for my soul which was pitching under the impulse of an uncertain weather—he laughed. His laughter was engaging, informed by an acute intelligence. He asked: "Are you *curious*?" Eagerly, I nodded. He turned and, taking a key from his pocket, opened an ebony cabinet faced with polished plate glass, where I saw the snake suspended anew in an identical jar. Smelling of camphor, the room was all at once cordial and ceremonial.

"In Egypt, once," he said, "very long ago, certain mystics insisted that it was feminine curiosity which precipitated the world." He pointed out two deep chairs. Expectant and relieved, Saida and I sat in that room where a thousand creatures were kept; a place which was, as Saida's bed, simultaneously diurnal and nocturnal.

First the professor pulled forth boxes two inches deep and tightly covered with glass. Here infinitesimal insects gummed to mica triangles glowed as elements in a vast chain of mythical associations: the corporealization of a lunar dew, the corneas of wizards, the lenses of another world. Next, settled deeper, were locusts—some surprisingly large and looking like the sacred vessels of a diminutive royalty. There were spiders also; the professor pointed out their mouths and multiple eyes. One was so enormous it could have been worn on the head of a child in guise of a velvet hat, a ceremonial hat sewn for an initiation into the darkest rites of the natural world, rites which my father had refused to name and number, but which I now know are numberless—and finite, too, for even as I write this, the world dies and the blue seeds of afterlife are only a sterile clay, after all.

Next, the professor showed us bottle fetuses, some like featureless lumps of wax, except that when looking closer one saw the fin-like hands and the faces on the verge of forming. There were eggs in quantity—yellow, black and blue; some were shaped like tops and some like whistles and one—the egg of a cuttlefish, I believe—looked like a corkscrew.

This cornucopic display thrust Saida and me into such a state of fearlessness that later in the blackening penumbra of her room, we lit a candle and took it under the sheets. It gilded us. Saida's vulva, as fuzzy as a peach, was crimson there where the fruit was sweetly incised. And it seemed, in those final hours when our mouths fused together and we sobbed with delight, that the *khamsin* raged within the room, that the air was a living wind in which bright things by the thousands agitated their wings.

222

Even years later, long after our fathers had cruelly fought and I was denied access to those rooms upon which a slip of the tongue had incurred malediction (in anger I had revealed that I had seen how even tyrants begin their lives as fish; how the world had not formed in seven days but, instead, slowly, painfully), I could feel Saida's mouth—the mouth of Venus Matutina, Venus Vesputina—pressed to the secret cipher between my legs, and I would fall back, as into the celestial void, and hear the stars tearing past, shredding the fabric of the night.

—For Salman Rushdie

LET MY PEOPLE GO

Diamanda Galas

The Devil has designed my death
and he's waiting to be sure
that plenty of his black sheep die
before he finds a cure.

O Lord Jesus, do you think I've served my time?
The eight legs of the Devil now are crawling up my
    spine.

The firm hand of the Devil now
is rocking me to sleep
I force my blind eyes open, Lord
But I'm sinking in the deep.

O Lord Jesus, do you think I've served my time?
The eight legs of the Devil now are crawling up my
    spine.

I go to sleep each evening now
dreaming of the grave

and see the friends I used to know
calling out my name.

O Lord Jesus, do you think I've served my time?
The eight legs of the Devil now are crawling up my
  spine.

O Lord Jesus, do you think I've served my time?
The eight legs of the Devil now are crawling up my
  spine.

O Lord Jesus, here's the news from those below:
The eight legs of the Devil will not let my people
  go.

224

LET'S NOT CHAT ABOUT DESPAIR

Diamanda Galas

You who speak of crowd control, of karma,
or the punishment of god:

Let's not chat about despair.

Do you fear the cages they are building in
Kentucky, Tennessee and Texas
while they're giving ten to forty years to find a cure?

Let's not chat about despair.

Do you pray each evening out of horror or of fear
to the savage God whose bloody hand
commands you now to die alone?

Let's not chat about despair.

Do you taste the presence of the living death
while the skeleton beneath your open window
waits with arms outstretched?

Let's not chat about despair.

Do you spend each night in waiting
for the devil's little angels' cries
to burn you in your sleep?

Let's not chat about despair.

Do you wait for miracles in small hotels
with Seconal and Compazine
226   or for a ticket to the house of death in Amsterdam?

Let's not chat about despair.

Do you wait in prison for the dreadful day
the office of the butcher comes to carry you away?

Let's not chat about despair.

Do you wait for saviors or the paradise to come
in laundry rooms, in toilets, or in cadillacs?

Let's not chat about despair.

Are you crucified beneath the life machines
with a shank inside your neck
and a head which blossoms like a basketball?

Let's not chat about despair.

Do you tremble at the timid steps
of crying, smiling faces who, in mourning,
now have come to pay their last respects?

Let's not chat about despair.

In Kentucky Harry buys a round of beer
to celebrate the death of Billy Smith, the queer,
whose mother still must hide her face in fear.

Let's not chat about despair.

You who mix the words of torture, suicide, and death
with scotch and soda at the bar,
we're all real decent people, aren't we,
but there's no time left for talk.

Let's not chat about despair.

PLEASE DON'T TALK ABOUT DESPAIR.

MALEDICTION

Diamanda Galas

The arms that you cut off that Sunday night
of the young man who ran screaming through the
   street,
streaming blood in trails of terror,
are the arms that point me to my door,
which forsaken by the blood of Jesus,
invites the Devil, who now waits for me outside.

The arms that you cut off that Sunday night
are the arms that point me to the red eyes
of the pentecostal killers and the black eyes
or the roman catholic killers and the blue eyes
of the pinhead skinhead killers,
and the dirty angel does his target practice night and
   day,
making ready now to steal my soul away.

The arms that you cut off that Sunday night
are the arms that wait between my T.V. and my gun,
while the winks and smiles of singing debutantes and
   eunuchs whisper,

"We don't want you. Unclean, lying there in vomit,
 filth and perspiration,
coming back with Jesus or with Elvis from the dead."

The arms that you cut off the body
of the screaming young man
dance before my eyes the endless murder of my soul
which, taunted every hour by open windows,
has kept itself alive with prayer,
but not for miracles,
and not for heaven.
Just for silence
and for mercy
until the end.

230

WERE YOU A WITNESS

Diamanda Galas

Were you a witness
Were you a witness

And on that holy day
And on that bloody day

Were you a witness
Were you a witness

And on that holy day
And on that bloody day
And on his dying bed he asked me;
"Tell all my friends I was fighting, too."
But to all cowards and voyeurs:

There are no more tickets to the funeral
There are no more tickets to the funeral

Were you a witness
Were you a witness

And on that holy day
And on that bloody day
There are no more tickets to the funeral
There are no more tickets to the funeral
The funeral is crowded.

Were you a witness
Were you a witness

232

Were you there when they crucified my Lord?
Were you there when they nailed him to the cross?
Sometimes it causes me to tremble, tremble, tremble
Were you there when they crucified my Lord?

Were you a witness?

Were you there when they dragged him to the grave?
Were you there when they dragged him to the grave?
Sometimes it causes me to wonder, wonder, wonder
Were you there when they dragged him to the grave?

Were you a witness?

Were you there when they laid him in the tomb?
Were you there when they laid him in the tomb?
Sometimes it causes me to wonder, wonder, wonder
Were you there when they laid him in the tomb?

And on that holy day
And on that bloody day
Were you a witness?

Swing Swing Swing

I looked over Jordan and what did I see
coming for to carry me home
A band of Angels coming after me
Coming for to carry me home

Swing Swing

A band of Devils! calling out my name
coming for to drag me to the grave

Swing

But I will not go
And I shall not go
I shall wake up and I shall walk from this room
into the sun
where the dirty angel doesn't run
where the dirty angel cannot go
and brothers in this time of pestilence do know

Each time that we meet we hear another sick man
  sigh
Each time that we meet we hear another man has
  died
And I see Angels Angels: Devils!
            Angels Angels: Devils!
            Angels Angels: Devils!
                    Coming for to carry me home.
Swing Swing

Mr. Sandman makes a filthy bed for me
But I shall not rest
And I will not rest
As a man who has been blinded by the storm

And waits for angels by the road
while the Devil waits for me at night
with knives and lies and smiles
and straps me down
and sings the *swing low sweet* chariot
of death knells
one by one like a sentence of the damned,
and one by one they come to warn me
of the *perils* of resistance,
and one by one of my brothers
die unsung unloved unwanted: Die!
and faster please
we've got no money for extended visits
  says the sandman

But we who have gone before
Do not rest in peace
We who have died
Shall never rest in peace

Remember me?
Unburied I am screaming in the bloody furnaces of
    hell
And only ask for you
to raise your weary eyes into the sun
until the sun has set
for we who have gone before do not rest in peace
We who have died
shall never rest in peace
There is no rest
until the fighting's done

And I see Angels Angels Devils!
        Angels Angels Devils!
        Angels Angels Devils!
        coming for to drag me to the grave

SECOND INVOCATION: SONO L'ANTICHRISTO

Diamanda Galas

Sono la prova.	I am the token.
Sono la salva.	I am the salvation.
Sono la carne macellata.	I am the butcher's meat.
Sono la sanzione.	I am the sanction.
Sono il sacrificio.	I am the sacrifice.
Sono il Ragno Nero.	I am the Black Spider.
Sono il scherno.	I am the scourge.
Sono la Santa Sede.	I am the Holy Fool.
Sono le feci dal Signore.	I am the shit of God.
Sono lo segno.	I am the sign.
Sono la pestilenza.	I am the plague.
Sono l'Antichristo.	I am the Antichrist.

BEST-SELLER

Michael Blumlein

OCTOBER 20

I once believed that poverty was a desirable state, a way for an artist to focus his mind, to distinguish the inessential from the essential. I was younger then and needed less. A simple room with a bed, a chair, a table. An old typewriter, some pencils, a stack of cheap paper. I prided myself on my economies, even though I could easily have found a job and lived otherwise. Asceticism seemed the proper breeding ground for a writer.

Things are different now. I have a family, and while poverty may serve some obscure personal purpose, I cannot accept it for my wife and son. They deserve better than recycled clothes and a tiny, dank apartment. Potato soup and week-old vegetables. Better than to hear me beg our landlord for a rent extension, or come home to a frigid apartment because the heat's been cut off. Indigence is no achievement. I hate being poor.

OCTOBER 21

Had a tough time with the book today. Dialogue felt flat, characters like they'd been collectively drugged. In the middle of asking myself what sense it meant to write something that didn't even hold my own interest, Tony called with the news that paperback rights to *In the Thicket* had been sold, but for only a fraction of what we'd hoped. And *Ordeal on the Neighbor's Lawn* has been remaindered. No big surprise but enough to put an end to today's work. Tony gently asked about the new book, and I answered in vague but enthusiastic terms. "Commercial potential" were, I think, the words I used. They sounded less threatening coming from me than Tony, but after we hung up, their meaning seemed as baffling as ever. What the hell do I have to do to write a book that sells?

OCTOBER 23

Nick goes through clothes like they were made of paper. Seems like every few days we're either patching something or making a trip to the Salvation Army. He's needed a new pair of shoes for a month now. I told him how Charlie Chaplin used a piece of bologna to patch a hole in his shoe in *Modern Times*. Nickie was intrigued.

"Where'd he get it?"

"From walking."

He looked at me, and I could see him thinking it through. "No," he said. "Where'd he get the bologna?"

OCTOBER 27

After a week of toothache that wouldn't quit, Claire broke down and went to the dentist. The guy wanted to do a root canal and put in some kind of bridge. Four hundred bucks. Claire told him to pull it. I was furious.

"I can't believe you let him do that. It's your body, Claire. Teeth don't grow back."

"I'm not stupid," she said.

"I can't believe it. Four hundred bucks. Did you tell the asshole we don't have that kind of money?"

"That's enough, Matt."

"Did you?"

"Matt," she said, stopping me with one of her looks. "I've got plenty left."

It's hard to stay mad at a woman like Claire. That look of hers is a killer. To tell the truth, she's kind of cute with a gap in the middle of her smile.

OCTOBER 29

Took Nick to the park after school, watched while he climbed the big cypress back of the tennis court. He's such a beauty, that boy. Nimble, fearless, reminded me of my own childhood, climbing like that. Young and invincible, one branch after another to the top of the tree. All sky up there. King of the world.

And even that time I fell, stepped on air instead of branch and plummeted twenty feet to the ground, even then something magical. Stunned, my rib cage vibrating like a string, I wandered through the forest in a trance. Finally made it home, bearing a lesson. The earth does not move when I strike it. Some things do not yield to my will.

Nick waved from the top of the cypress, and I caught myself praying he did not have to fall, hoping there was some other, easier way to learn.

On the way home he kept lagging behind. Said his leg hurt. Damn shoes, he probably got hung up coming down the tree. I promised we'd get a new pair as soon as a check comes.

242

NOVEMBER 1

Claire called from work in a state. They doubled the number of calls she has to take per hour, which of course makes the callers even angrier than they were to begin with. I took a break from the book and met her for lunch. She was nearly in tears.

"Some of the people are so rude. Over a goddamned dishwasher or some stupid toaster oven. Like their machine is more important than I am."

"Quit," I told her.

"This woman called today to complain that her husband's shirts weren't getting white enough. He's mad at her because he doesn't have a clean shirt to wear to work. So she calls and gets mad at me. Can you believe it?"

"What did you say to her?"

"I went through the whole routine, but she didn't want to hear. She just wanted to be mad. I don't need it."

"Everyone's mad," I said. "Quit."

"Don't keep saying that."

"You hate it."

"What I hate is when you make things sound so simple. It's like you're trying to fool me. You're telling a lie."

"It's no lie, Claire."

She looked away. "I'm not in the mood for this."

"Other people are just like us. They want their lives to live up to their dreams. They're trying to find a little hope."

"I can't believe yelling at me possibly helps." She shook her head and grumbled, eventually dismissing the subject with a sigh. "Did you work today?"

"It was like pulling teeth, if you'll excuse the expression."

She didn't smile. "Has Tony seen any of it?"

"A couple of chapters. He thinks we can make some money. At least as much as *Thicket*."

"Not exactly a rousing endorsement."

"Forget Tony. We'll make money. If we don't, I'll find another way."

"Sure you will."

"I mean it."

She regarded me queerly, then took out her compact and freshened up her lips. After she'd gone, I stayed at the table, thinking over what I'd said. When I was a boy the possibilities of success abounded, but as an adult I find that same world far more difficult to locate. Nevertheless, my ambition remains fierce. This worries me sometimes. Am I lying to myself, as Claire seems to think? Could I ever truly give up writing?

NOVEMBER 4
Up day today. Words flew onto the page in a fury. Finished Chapter 11, and for the first time everything seems in place. Jaime's beginning to come around . . . by the end he will have redeemed himself. The marriage of hope to sadness, a fitting conclusion. And just the kind of thing that'll sell.

NOVEMBER 5
Nick complains about his leg. Still tender where he fell, and he limps ever so slightly. Funny, when I was a kid, seems like I recovered from bumps and bruises overnight. Maybe it's just growing pains. Anyway, I gave him a couple of aspirin, which seemed to help. If he's not better by the time Claire gets her paycheck, I'll take him to the doctor.

NOVEMBER 8
During a lull in the writing found myself looking through the want ads. All sorts of job opportunities and the accompanying visions of wealth. I let myself go, imagining the great adventures I could have as a filing clerk, memorizing long series of numbers, breathing paper dust and filing one folder after another. Or as a loan processor, recipient of all the

hope and loathing people extend onto agents of finance. A cook perhaps, knowing as I do the masterly craft of opening cans and heating their contents. Or a secretary, typing with clumsy fingers and answering the phone with cloaked civility. There was an opening for a librarian that sounded appealing, and on a whim I dialed the number. The woman, though pleasant, was unimpressed by the fact that I was a published author. In fact, in some subtle way she seemed to hold it against me, as though I would be the last person on earth capable of helping a reader. When she discovered I lacked the proper college degree, she advised me not to apply for the job and hung up. Her rejection upset me, and I quickly dialed another number, choosing an advertisement at random just to prove that I was at least capable of getting past a phone call. A man came on the line and when I told him I was interested in a job, he asked if I had experience with the DBX 2000, the TAC 143, the QT 1522 and the BRT 6200. After a slight pause I told him yes, I did have some knowledge of car engines, having worked extensively on my old Toyota before it blew a head gasket and died a year ago. There was a brief silence on his end of the line, and then he said he wasn't looking for jokers and hung up.

I was deflated, feeling in some strange way that my manhood had been insulted. With unexpected determination I searched the ads for anything to assuage my injured pride. Past dental assistants, escorts and car salesmen. Machinists, cosmetic counterpersons, TV repairmen. None were remotely possible and I was about to give up when my eyes caught a box at the bottom of the page. "DONORS NEEDED," it read. "Good health the only requirement."

I called the number, and the most delightful woman answered. She represented a medical organization that was conducting a study, and if I was in good health she would be happy to set up an appointment for an interview. Upon further questioning, she explained that their research was in the field of organ transplantation, though she was quick to reassure me that the study required only a questionnaire and simple blood test. They were offering $200 to all those who enrolled. She concluded by saying, rather cryptically, that under the right circumstances there was the opportunity for lucrative, full-time employment.

Her persuasiveness was such that I was about to make an appointment, when I realized that I had never really intended to go through with any of this. My whim had taken me further than I intended.

Thanking her, I hung up, disturbed at how close I had been to substituting some other project for the book. There's no question that money's tight, but we'll get by. The book will be finished before long, and once it sells we'll get out of this rattrap life for good.

NOVEMBER 9
Walked down by the wharf this afternoon, reconstituting after a rough morning. The sharp, briny smell of salt water and fish was a tonic. The one-armed man at Scoma's, the big Italian with the crooked nose, was dumping palletfuls of crab into his chest-high vat of

boiling water. Fat, pink claws, severed from their bodies, floated to the surface.

I started to order one for dinner, then stopped when I realized the price. Instead, I bought a bag of fish guts and a couple of old heads, thinking soup. But I couldn't bring myself to do it and ended up feeding the slop to some seals, who barked and clapped their flippers appreciatively.

On the way home I passed a quadriplegic woman playing piano with her tongue. A newspaper clipping tacked on a board behind her told how she was a single mom supporting two kids. She did a nice job, particularly a moving rendition of "Amazing Grace." Big hit with the tourists. I overheard someone say what courage she must have. Yes, I thought. Undeniably. And yet it occurred to me that she's only doing what she has to, what she knows, to survive.

NOVEMBER 11
Nick's leg no better so took him to the hospital today. Doctor ordered an X ray and a blood test. Said there was something wrong in the bone but he wasn't sure what. Wants to do another test next week, some kind of scan of the bone. I asked if it was absolutely necessary and the look he gave me made me feel unfit to be alive. Of course we'll do the test. That's about it for Claire's paycheck.

NOVEMBER 12
Had a sweet lovemaking with Claire. It's been a while. Unseasonably warm night kept us from having to

huddle under blankets. She has such a beautiful body, the swale of her belly like some flawless planet, a geography made all the more perfect by the pale thin scar half-hidden in her pubic hair where the doctors cut her open to deliver Nick. She told me once she had feared an ugly scar more than the surgery itself. She's still self-conscious, even though it's barely visible. She rarely lets me touch it, and I've stopped telling her it's as lovely as any of her natural landmarks. Lovelier, because it reminds me of her courage. She doesn't believe me.

Instead, I ask myself if I would have the same courage, given the opportunity. What would require it? Scars do not bother me. Nor am I especially frightened by the possibility of bodily injury. Some threat to my son? My wife? Undoubtedly. But for myself, only myself, what terrifies most is failure. It haunts my inner life, and I do whatever I can to avoid it. My act of courage, if it ever comes, will be to abandon ambition forever.

NOVEMBER 14

Finished Chapter 12, one more to go. Even at this late stage there are surprises. Jaime turned unexpectedly dour, revealing a side to himself that augurs darkly for the book. Suggests an ending I'd hoped to avoid. People are willing to consider suffering but only as a tonic. Redemption must prevail.

But this book will be a success, I swear it. By the end Jaime will reveal yet another layer, a deeper one.

A wellspring of faith and abiding love. I know it's there. Even the hardest hearts will weep.

NOVEMBER 15

I came home today to find Claire yelling at Nick. He was standing beside the refrigerator, cowering and trying not to cry. Between them on the floor lay a mess of broken eggs. Claire lifted him roughly by the arms and moved him to the side. In a voice shaking with anger she ordered him to his room.

When he was gone, I asked what had happened. She gave me a bleak look, then knelt on the floor and buried her face in her hands.

"I hate this," she muttered. "I hate it, hate it, hate it."

"I'll get some more."

She looked up accusingly. "With what?"

"You don't have to take it out on Nick."

She started to reply, then her eyes filled with tears.

"Claire . . ."

She waved me away. "How does it get like this? Suddenly you see yourself doing something you never dreamed you could. That awful glimpse. The shame . . ."

"Talk to him. Tell him."

"I wish we had money."

"We will."

"I don't mean a lot. Some." Wearily, she got to her feet. "It's not his fault."

She left the kitchen, and I stared at the mess. Half

a dozen broken eggs is not a pretty sight. My responsibility? Maybe so.

Taking the rag in hand, I cleaned the floor, then went and found that ad in the newspaper. The same woman answered the phone, same cordial, pleasant voice, as though she were the guardian of some secret of contentment and happiness. I made the appointment to give her my blood.

NOVEMBER 16

The monkey sits on our head, we sit on the monkey. I finish the book, and an hour later the doctor calls to say that Nickie has cancer. Cancer. What is the heart to do? Between exhilaration at completing the book and this sudden grief, my heart chooses the latter. It is my son. They want to cut off his leg.

NOVEMBER 20

Another battery of tests. Doctors now unsure whether to amputate or try to cure with radiation and drugs. We are nearly broke. The $200 I'll have after tomorrow will stake us to another week, maybe two if we stretch it. Medical bills will just have to wait. By the time we get the second collection notice the book should be sold.

NOVEMBER 21

The question of worthiness plagues me. Am I a good husband? A father? A writer? In moments of clarity I see fame as the culmination of fear, success another name for sacrifice. Ambition has a way of being un-forgiving.

The appointment was on Larkin Street, in a fancy old apartment building on Russian Hill. Its entrance was framed by marble pillars and lined by enormous stone urns the color of sand. At the top of the stairs was a glass door with a polished brass casing and a single doorbell. I was buzzed inside by a uniformed guard who asked my business. I gave him my name, which he checked on a clipboard before pointing me to a door at the rear of the lobby. It opened onto an old-fashioned elevator with a hand-operated metal gate. There were eight floors to the building and I took the elevator to the top, where I stepped out into a carpet-lined hallway lit by a single large chandelier. Opposite me was a door with the number I'd been given.

A blue-suited man with a pleasant, generically hand-some face let me in, addressing me by name without bothering to introduce himself. He was a head taller than me and at least that much wider across the shoulders. His handshake was just firm enough to enforce the already unmistakable impression of latent strength.

He led me through a door into a second room many times larger than the first, full of furniture, sculptures and paintings. I recognized a Van Gogh, marveling at the quality of the reproduction until I realized that it was probably the original. A brass head I had once seen in an art book lay casually propped on a table.

Beside it was a richly upholstered couch and at the far end of the room a grand piano, its black top gleaming.

The opulence was overwhelming, and it was some time before I ventured away from the door. Mindful of all the precious objects, I crossed to a picture window on the other side of the room. It was a relief to look out, like having a sip of plain water after a meal of sweets.

The view was breathtaking. To the west lay the city, to the north the bay, its water gray in the blunted afternoon light. I had the impression I was staring out from a gigantic eye, far from the poverty to which I was accustomed. It was a safe, antiseptic view, and for an instant the sun broke through the clouds, throwing a bright slit of light across the water. In that moment of beauty I forgot my sorrow, but then a door closed, breaking the reverie.

I turned, expecting to see the totem-like man who had ushered me in. Instead, it was a woman. She had a youngish look about her but moved with the deliberation of someone older. She wore a skirt and open-necked blouse, and her skin was either lightly tanned or else naturally dark. She introduced herself simply as Devora, and as soon as she spoke I recognized the voice of the woman on the telephone.

We sat opposite each other on the sofa, and I casually remarked that it was a beautiful room, not at all what I'd expected for a medical interview. She replied that there was no reason for research to be conducted in austerity and went on to explain that the foundation she represented was small and personal enough to be attentive to such niceties.

"Those who work for us suffer few hardships," she said, then opened a folder on her lap and began with her questions.

Most pertained to my health but others concerned my family, marriage, even my financial situation. Some were quite personal, and initially I was reluctant to discuss them. Devora was an attractive woman, her nails meticulously manicured, her hair just so. She wore several thin gold necklaces, which she had a habit of twirling through her fingers, a mannerism that, taken with her scrupulous beauty, called to mind a vanity that did not inspire trust. In every other way, though, she seemed open and sincere, so that after a while I found myself willing to confide in her. I spoke briefly of my troubled career as a writer, my aspirations and current hopes for success. I mentioned Claire's dissatisfaction with work and, after a moment's hesitation, told her of the tumor in Nickie's leg. She made a note on her paper, then closed the folder and rewarded me with a look of sympathy and understanding.

253

"The human body can be so fragile," she said. "I'm very sorry."

"The doctors talk of a cure."

"Of course."

"He's receiving radiation and drugs. We're very hopeful."

"Certainly. And if the boy does not respond. What then?"

I was taken aback. "What kind of a question is that?"

"You must have considered it."

"It's none of your business."

"Forgive me."

A silence ensued, which she seemed in no hurry to break.

"They'll have to cut it off," I muttered. "Give him some sort of fake leg."

"A prosthesis."

I nodded.

"If it were possible for your son to receive a real leg, one of flesh and blood, would you consent?"

"I don't understand."

"A living limb. A transplant."

"The doctors have never mentioned that."

"The operation is rarely done," she said authoritatively. "The donor requirements are so strict as to virtually prohibit it."

"Then why do you ask?"

"The foundation is interested in the attitudes people have toward transplantation."

"It must be expensive."

"Forgetting the cost."

I gave her a look.

"Come now. You're a writer. A thinker. Take it as a philosophical question." She played with a necklace. "If a limb were available, if it could be grafted on, would you consent?"

I sensed that some trap was being laid, but she did not seem the type. Still, I felt the need to consider carefully. I stood and walked to the window. The clouds now covered the whole of the city, bathing it in a marbled, celestial light.

"Yes," I said at length. "I'd consent. What father would not want his child whole?"

"It is a great gift."

"You have children?"

"One," she said without elaboration. She looked at her watch, then stood and smoothed her skirt. "You've been very patient."

She led me to a door opposite the one she had entered and motioned me inside. When I realized she was not going to follow, I stopped and asked about the money.

"You'll receive a check within the week."

255

I hesitated briefly before asking if there was some way to be paid sooner. She started to say one thing, then stopped herself.

"Of course. I'll take care of it. And again, many thanks for your cooperation."

She left, leaving me alone in this new room. It was small and windowless, unpleasantly lit by a fluorescent rectangle of overhead light. In the center was a narrow table, on either side of which was an armless plastic chair. In one corner was a sink and in another, a refrigerator. Black-and-white photographs graced the walls, highly magnified views of people's faces. I was studying the lobe of an ear when a man entered the room. He wore a white lab coat and looked uncannily like the man I had first met. He had me sit opposite him at the table, then opened a drawer and brought out a needle, syringe and tourniquet. After tying the tourniquet around my arm, he slid the needle swiftly into a vein, causing the barest whisper of pain, and drew off five or six tubes of blood. He finished almost as soon as he had started, releasing the tourniquet and pasting a small Band-Aid on top of the puncture wound. He marked the tubes with a pen, aligned them in a metal rack at the end of the table, then stood up with the rack in hand. He thanked me and pointed to a door, then turned and exited by another. Opening the one he had indicated, I found myself in the very first room I had entered.

I was disoriented, and stood for a moment wondering what to do. Just then, yet another door opened and the man in the blue suit who had first greeted me appeared. From his vest pocket he took out a plain white envelope, which he handed to me. I was embarrassed to look but felt foolish not to, and ended up turning my back and quickly checking the contents. Satisfied, I slid the envelope in my coat pocket, thanked him and left.

In the elevator I looked in the envelope again. Four fifty-dollar bills, as crisp as crackers. Easy money. It made me want to come back.

NOVEMBER 29

Tony is lukewarm on the book. He tries to be kind, says things like "it's idiosyncratic. Challenging." He wants more of a resolution, meaning, if not complete sunshine, at least a healthy glow of happiness at the end. "Does Jaime have to suffer so much?" he asks. I feel like telling him to ask Jaime, instead reply that suffering is the human condition, is only a small step on the larger road to enlightenment. I tell him this is a story about love and love involves sacrifice.

"We're just a breath away from paradise here," I hear myself saying. "Let the people judge. They've learned from their soap operas. They know how to pick a winner."

NOVEMBER 30

Got a letter from Devora and the Kingman Foundation today. Says if I'm interested in further work to give them a call. I'm not. The conversation yesterday with Tony has left me surprisingly upbeat about my chances with the book. I'm a writer. I'll wait.

DECEMBER 6

Nick is brave as hell. He limps all the time, obviously in pain, but he hardly ever complains. Worst thing for him is not being able to go out with the guys after school. By then he's so exhausted he has to come home for a nap. Sleeps until dinner. His appetite's off, doctors say the treatments will do that. Claire's a wreck, seeing him like this. Like a part of herself has ceased to function properly. I'm not much better. We're barely eating, waking five, six times a night out of worry. This thing's a family disease.

DECEMBER 11

Met with Nick's doctors today. Grave men, but humane. Treatment not going as well as they'd hoped.

Nick can't tolerate the doses they need to eradicate the tumor. All agree to give it another couple of weeks. If no response, amputation.

I asked about a transplant. Difficult, they say, much harder than kidney or even heart. Cadavers don't work, donor has to be living and vital. Limbs remain viable for less than an hour after death.

"Obviously hard to find a living person willing to part with his leg," says one of the doctors.

"Prosthetics are getting better all the time," says another.

I ask about cost.

"A lot," says the doctor in charge.

"What? A hundred thousand?"

"More."

"Two?"

"After it's all over, probably half a million."

A daunting figure. I glance at Claire, who's staring at the floor, trying to contain herself. Anger rises in me, and then from nowhere an overwhelming sense of failure. Irrational as it is, I feel responsible.

DECEMBER 13

The city is filled with the smoke from a brush fire a hundred miles to the east. Tiny white ashes float in the air, as though this were the day of judgment. People go methodically about their business without the slightest concern. I myself feel at the mercy of circumstances beyond my control, ironically the first breath of fresh air in months.

We are dead broke. It's a kind of freedom. Stark,

but unencumbered by the swamp of egotism and pride. Now I have no choice but to get a job. I spread the want ads on the floor, poised with my foot to stamp at random, when the phone rings. It's Devora.

"You received our letter?" she asks.

"Letter?" I'm about to hang up when I remember.

"We like to call to be sure," she says smoothly.

"Nicholas," I reply, embarrassed at my forgetfulness. "I've been preoccupied."

"I understand."

Do you, I want to say, angry suddenly at her wealth and good health. Instead, I glance down at the newsprint under my foot. An ad for a school of technical and creative writing, promising exciting and rewarding careers. The ultimate self-indictment.

I tell her I'll take the job.

259

DECEMBER 23

It's a funny kind of work. I've been poked and prodded by three different doctors, scanned by at least twice that many machines, had tubes passed down my throat and up my ass, blood drawn, eyes and ears checked, exercised, rested . . . it goes on. Some of the tests are done in the Larkin Street apartment, but most in a private and fancy little clinic near Mission Bay. Everyone's nice as can be, making me feel a bit guilty. These tests would cost anyone else thousands, and here I am getting paid to do them. And paid handsomely. It's the easiest money I've ever earned.

As Devora has explained it, the foundation's work is in the area of clinical transplantation, and according to her, they've been highly successful. My job, after this initial phase, will be to provide certain materials, such as hair and skin, for grafting. My tissues have been matched to another man, who will receive them. Although the work will be intermittent, as long as I remain available my salary will continue. Raises, she promises, will be frequent and generous.

JANUARY 22
It's been nearly a month now, and I've yet to be called on. From time to time I find myself wondering what it will be . . . a small piece of skin, a tuft of hair? For the most part, though, I've been too busy to think about it.

260   We've moved into a beautiful new apartment at the tip of Grant Avenue. Three bedrooms, big kitchen and a living room with a fireplace and a spectacular view of the bay. I spend hours just sitting in my armchair, beer in hand, luxuriating in the warmth of a well-heated room and the panorama of sky and water. We bought a television and VCR for Nickie to use while he's going through the exercises with his new leg. He's doing remarkably well considering the amputation was little more than a month ago. Stump's all healed, he's got his energy back, raring to go. Amazing how he bounces back.

No word yet about the book, and other than these entries I'm not writing. I'm making good money as it is. Why torture myself to be rejected?

JANUARY 31

I was called today for my first "assignment." A few tufts of hair from the back part of my scalp. They use an instrument that looks a little like an apple corer, but much smaller. Because my hair is so thick the missing spots are hardly visible. The whole thing lasted about an hour and now I am back home, sucking on a beer and watching the rain sweep across the city. It's a lovely sight, and I feel no need to improve on it.

FEBRUARY 10

Lately, I've been wondering about the man on the other end. Devora says someday I'll meet him, though she seems in no particular hurry. I gather he's quite a bit older and not in the best of health. Selfishly, I find myself hoping that, even in sickness, he survives a long time.

The part of my scalp where they took the hair is virtually healed. The scabs came off yesterday, which makes the itching much less. The rectangle of skin from my inner thigh, however, is another matter. They used something called a microtome, which supposedly takes off only the thinnest of layers, but it feels as if they branded me with an iron. The area is all red and hurts like hell to touch. I haven't been able to go out because my pants rub against it. No sex all this week.

FEBRUARY 15

Second week and skin graft still not healed. Somehow it got infected, which isn't supposed to happen. Now I'm on antibiotics and bed rest to air it out. The doctors couldn't be nicer, but I'm not used to being sick. Makes me cantankerous. To top it off Tony called with bad news. Because of disappointing sales of my first two books, they're not making an offer on the new one. Fine, I say. Let them wither in the heat of my future fame and success.

FEBRUARY 20

Damn sore finally healed enough that Claire could touch me without my feeling she was sticking a knife in my leg. We made love gingerly, despite the weeks of pent up desire. Afterwards, I found myself unconsciously fingering the scar on her belly. She didn't seem to mind, maybe because she was busy trying to arouse me again.

"This stays," she said.

"You bet."

"I mean it. It's one part I'll never let them take." Her face was hidden, and I couldn't tell if she was joking. The idea sent shivers down my spine.

FEBRUARY 24

I met Kingman Ho today, after whom the foundation is named. A tall man with a face that was once probably handsome, he was looking out the big picture window in the living room when I arrived. Devora introduced us, and I held out a hand that he did not immediately take. Instead, he looked at me from behind his thick glasses with eyes that were impossible to read. I remembered gazing out over the city on my first visit, thinking it lovely though distant and dreamlike. The feeling I had as he looked at me was much the same but in reverse, as though I were a landscape of his own imagination. Either that or an article of clothing he was appraising.

It made me uncomfortable and I became conscious of my imperfections, the faint scar on my cheek from a boyhood accident, the part of my nose that was broken in a fall. For some reason I felt I should apologize, but instead I mumbled some inane comment about the view. He looked at me quizzically, as if surprised that I was capable of speech, and turned to Devora, who whispered something in his ear. He nodded and managed to smile at me, then left the room. Devora adjusted one of the necklaces at her throat.

"He likes you," she said, an assessment that seemed beyond the realm of anyone's knowledge. I asked what made her say so.

"He has no choice," she replied. "Kingman is ill. You may have noticed."

"He seemed distant."

"Renal osteodystrophy," she said cryptically. "His bones are like eggshells."

"He's in pain?"

"Great pain," she said. "Seldom will you ever meet a braver man."

I thought of Nick, who more than once has humbled me with his courage.

"My son is brave."

She stared out the window, nodding ever so slightly.

"They say that courage is contagious. How is the boy doing?"

"Well. He's already walking."

"The money is sufficient? There's been no interference with his care?"

"You've been more than generous."

She nodded again, this time turning to face me. "They say that that, too, is contagious."

She left the room before I had a chance to ask what she meant, and a moment later I followed, ushered out by the man in the blue suit.

At home tonight I looked up the disease in a book. Something having to do with kidney failure, the bones becoming wafer thin because all the calcium leaches out. Later on in bed, I found myself rubbing my flank, and Claire, sensing that something was troubling me, stilled me with her hand. Then she kissed where I had been rubbing, outlining the area with her tongue, as if to describe a future scar to match her own. An uncanny woman, choosing just the right moment to show her tenderness.

"I love you no matter who you are," she murmured, as she has so many times before. It makes all the difference.

FEBRUARY 27

Devora dropped by today, ostensibly to see the apartment and meet Claire. She wore a gay-looking dress with a scooped collar and the omnipresent gold chains at her throat. Claire was cordial but ill at ease, and I could tell from the beginning she was waiting for the visit to be over. At a certain point she excused herself to make tea, and Devora used the opportunity to inform me of some upcoming work. At the same time she handed me a "bonus" check of $5,000. I stared at it for a moment, then folded it and put it away.

"Please don't mention this to Claire," I said, sensing it was unnecessary to ask. "It's always been hard for her to accept good fortune. I'll tell her later."

"Be politic when you do," said Devora. "I don't want her to fear me more than she does."

"What she fears is the sudden wealth."

"Perhaps." She was pensive. "And you?"

"I fear that it will end."

MARCH 8

A week now since they took the kidney. Except for some pain when I turn or move fast, I don't even notice that it's gone. The initial shock of being asked to part with it has passed. So, too, the surprise that the recipient is Kingman Ho himself. Wealth makes its own rules. I look at it like this: if Nickie or Claire needed a kidney in order to live, would I offer one of mine? Without a second thought. So isn't what I'm giving them now nearly the same? A decent place to live, food when they're hungry, heat, clothing. By donating my kidney to Ho, I'm simply giving my family a life they deserve.

MARCH 21

Attended a small party at the Larkin Street apartment this evening. After considerable persuasion Claire agreed to come, and Nick joined us. We were met by the nameless man in the blue suit, who took our coats and ushered us into the living room. Devora stood beside the piano, drink in hand, talking to a woman who might well have been her twin. Kingman Ho was nearby, surrounded by a clump of judicious-looking, well-tailored men. Several couples stood at the window, taking in the magnificent view, and beyond them, warming themselves by the fireplace, two of the doctors who had examined me. A servant in a starched black dress brought us drinks, and a few minutes later a girl served us hors d'oeuvres from a silver tray. She couldn't have been more than a year or two older than Nick, though her manners were those of an adult well trained in service. She held out the tray to Nickie, who didn't quite know what to do. He looked to me for help, while the girl, in complete possession of herself, urged him to take one of her tidbits. I nodded my approval, then took one myself, a bit of cracker heaped generously with caviar. It was delicious, and I had another.

At length Devora came over with Kingman, clinging unashamedly to him as if he were some prize catch. I did not immediately grasp the significance of this. Admittedly, the man looked fitter than before, his color better, his attention crisper, but his stolid manner seemed a world away from Devora's youthfulness and vigor. She was a good twenty, even thirty years his junior, yet here she was nuzzling his neck like some restless colt. It occurred to me she might be his daughter, yet her attentions seemed anything but filial.

Kingman greeted me with more warmth than when we had first met. He held my hand longer than was necessary, using the opportunity to once again appraise me. This time I returned his scrutiny, and after a moment he smiled, releasing me with a muttered word of appreciation. He introduced himself to Claire, gracefully slipping her hand through his arm and steering her away.

"He seems to have recovered his health," I said drily.

"Remarkably," replied Devora, looking after him. "He's a new man."

"Perhaps I should be flattered."

She considered this, then took a step closer. She was a little drunk. "For the first time in years he performs like a man." She touched a necklace, smiling to herself. "I had all but forgotten. Imagine. Now I am called on to be a woman again. Who would have thought?"

"I'm happy for you," I said, but in truth I was not. It seemed wrong that Ho, already so much older than she, was performing with a body not wholly his. More than that, it seemed improper, as though I were being used in some strange and undignified way as a sex surrogate. This I had never agreed to, and I was about to say something when Devora's look-alike interrupted us. She introduced herself, and I casually asked if the two of them were twins.

"You flatter me," said Devora.

"My mother knows the secret of youth," said the woman. She brushed a piece of stray hair from Devora's cheek and whispered something in her ear. Devora nodded and the woman, excusing herself, left.

"Mother?" I said. "To her? She can't be less than thirty."

"A beautiful girl," said Devora proudly.

"How old are you?"

She smiled coyly, touching one of her necklaces. Just then a piece of wood caught fire, momentarily brightening the room. It cast a sudden light on her throat, revealing a thin white scar at the base of her neck. I stared at it, then her eyes. They were laughing at me.

"The others are well hidden," she said.

"I'm embarrassed."

"Don't be." She lifted a glass of wine from a passing tray, holding it aloft as if in a toast. "What greater act of creation than to create ourselves?"

Later that evening, watching the fog slip through the gate, I happened to catch Nick out of the corner of an eye. He was sitting on the floor at the far end of the room, partially obscured by one of the piano legs. Kneeling next to him was the serving girl. At first I thought they were playing some game, so rapt were they, but after edging a little closer, I saw they were doing something entirely different. Nick had his pant leg rolled up, and the girl was fingering his prosthesis. Inch by inch she was creeping up the leg, circling it one moment, stroking it the next, coddling it as though she were unearthing some priceless relic.

Nick was utterly entranced, as mesmerized by the girl's attention as she was by his false limb. When she came to the edge of his pant leg, she'd stop and glance up, waiting for him to roll the pants up farther. Little by little the entire limb was being exposed.

By the look on his face Nick seemed actually to be feeling the girl's touch, as though the intensity of her exploration were awakening some hitherto slumbering receptors in his phantom limb. There was a charge I could feel from across the room.

I was torn about what to do, feeling on the one hand that it was my responsibility as a father to intervene and on the other that to interrupt now might only reinforce the stigma of Nickie's handicap. The choice was made moot when one of the adult servants found the girl and with angry words pulled her from the room. The spell broken, Nickie became suddenly self-conscious, fumbling abashedly with his pant leg. I rushed over and helped him to his feet, saying nothing of what I had seen. I suggested it was time to leave, and, after looking quickly around the room, presumably for the girl, Nick agreed. I had an arm on his shoulder but he shrugged me off, preferring to make his exit alone.

He fell asleep in the car on the way home, but a parent can never be sure. I decided to hold off telling Claire of the incident, and to pass the time I asked her opinion of Kingman Ho. They had spent nearly an hour together.

"I think there's something terribly wrong with him," she said. "We weren't together for ten minutes before

I wanted to comfort him. A complete stranger. It's not what I expected."

"Suffering has a certain allure. Ho's been ill with one thing or another for years."

"When he speaks of himself, it's as though he were someone else. Once he said something, I don't remember what, and I found myself thinking, this is a man who lives in a mirror. A brittle, distant mirror."

"He's arrogant. And rich. I think he makes a point of staying aloof."

"He told me he holds himself in contempt. I asked him why and he said for lacking the strength to die."

"He's posing, Claire. It's cocktail party conversation."

"He scares me," she said, shivering against the cold and pulling Nick towards her. "I wish we didn't depend on him."

"You have it backwards," I told her, angry that she had been affected this way. "I'm the one who holds the aces. Kingman Ho depends on me."

MAY 3

Last month it was the small bones in my ear. A week later, my right eye. It's amazing how quickly I adapt. Unless someone whispers to my left, I hear almost as well as before. And except for a certain flatness of vision, which becomes less noticeable each day, my eyesight is unchanged.

I run into Ho from time to time. He is polite, even cordial, and ironically I'm now the one who's keeping a distance. There's little I have to say to him, and what

I do usually comes out rudely. The fact is that I don't like him. He takes and takes like a spoiled child, and what does he give in return? Money. It's a cold reward.

Nevertheless, when we meet, I look for signs in him of recognition. I often find myself staring at his right eye, the brown one stippled with green, the one that is mine. It looks stony in his face, callous, yet every so often it takes on a gleam too familiar to ignore. I know your motives, it seems to say. You cannot lie.

Sometimes I want to claw the eye from his face.

MAY 5
Tony called . . . another rejection. I told him I don't care. For the first time that I remember I feel liberated from the yoke of the marketplace.

MAY 17
There is something erotic about all this. It embarrasses me to say so because it sounds perverse. Yet each time they take part of my body, my sexuality becomes heightened. The toes were taken a week and a half ago, and since then I've been in a state of constant erection, having wet dreams nearly every night. Claire, always before my sexual match, has been eclipsed by this newfound desire. It's as if my unconscious self, fearful of its survival, has panicked, triggering a surge of sexuality in the hopes of perpetuating my genetic stock before I suffer extinction.

At times I have the feeling I am approaching a new and primitive state, one of explosive creativity and gratification. The compulsion for language and

abstract thought has become remote, making me
wonder why I ever bothered writing at all. In compari-
son to the language of the body, words say so little.

Claire, who knows me perhaps better than I know
myself, thinks I'm a little mad.

MAY 23
They want my arm. My right arm. Shoulder to
fingertip. I'm afraid.

MAY 31
This past week has felt like a year. The fear of apprehension is with me constantly. The blue-suited body-
guard will appear, blandly crushing me in his arms
and taking me back. Or Devora will arrive, bearing
some new manner of persuasion. A subtle change of
posture, a lilt in her voice, the veiled promise of some
favor impossible to refuse. Or Kingman himself, man
of few words, instigator of my flight. Armless now,
with no finger to pull the trigger, no hand to make
me dance at his insane command. He will come to
beg for my limb.

Let him. Let him feel my contempt at his wealth
and power. He is not a man. No man would do to me
what he has done.

More than anything, I fear my own uncertainty. I
could tell them I'm through and put a stop to this
thing once and for all. Or else give them the arm and
be done with it. Why run?

Wealth and success are not easy to dismiss. What

if Kingman dies? Kingman the Brute, the Cruel. My patron. What then?

JUNE 3
The wind howls in the canyons, scouring the earth with sand. The heat of the desert sun is unbelievable. I hide in my motel room and wait. I'm convinced they know where I am. Why don't they come?

JUNE 5
One's self-importance diminishes greatly out here. The desert is too big, too raw and exposed to suffer pride and deceit. I see that my hatred for Ho is little more than the mirage of my own inadequacy. I cannot despise him for wanting my arm any more than I can despise my son for wanting a new leg. It's man's nature to fight disintegration and decay.

273

But more, I begin to see that Kingman Ho and I are linked. Each layer of skin, each organ that I give weds him more firmly to me. Ho is my creation. Running from him is tantamount to running from myself.

JUNE 29
Absence is a stronger state than presence. It derives shape from the imagination, from loss and need. The arm has been gone for weeks, but when I close my eyes it is still there. I feel sensations in thin air, pain, heat, motion. I hold a pencil, a cup of coffee in a phantom world, stroke Claire's back and feel the texture of her skin with a hand that can't be seen. But

something exists, I know it, something that could not be severed from the tracts of memory.

I imagine the arm hanging from Kingman's side, attached to his nerves and muscles, moving to his command but all the while maintaining a deeper program, untempered by conscious thought. I picture the hand accentuating the air with my mannerisms, writing in my script, stroking Devora with my touch. The limb is a ghost and I the ghost writer. As I serve Kingman, he serves me.

JULY 2
We have more money now than we know what to do with. Claire has quit her job, and Nick has private tutors to help him make up the time he's lost. I read rather than write, or else sit in the armchair with a beer and watch the bay change colors. I don't feel lazy. My job is to heal.

JULY 15
It's surprising how fast I recover from these operations. Just a few days ago they took a piece of bone from my pelvis, and already I'm able to move around quite well. Except for the skin graft months ago, I've had no problems whatever. I can't say the same for Kingman. Even though our tissues are matched, he still seems to struggle through almost every procedure. His age must have something to do with it, and Devora says the drugs he takes to keep from rejecting my tissue get in the way of his healing. It's hard to see anyone suffer as he does. I pity him and sometimes

wonder why he persists. Does he truly fear death, or is there some other reason that he prolongs his life? Perhaps immortality is a motive in itself.

JULY 18

Woke up from a dead sleep last night wondering, of all things, what Kingman had for dinner. Not simply the menu but how he had eaten, and with whom. Was it a lively, high-spirited meal or tiresomely dull, a pleasure or, in his old age, a chore? Did he eat alone or with company? In suit and tie or more casually? What did he say? What did he think and not say?

It took me an hour to get back to sleep, and in the morning I needed two cups of coffee to wake up. As I poured the second, I tried to remember if I'd ever seen Kingman drink coffee. Black or with cream? One cup or two?

JULY 21

Why haven't they called? It's been nearly a week without a word. Something bad has happened, I know it. Two things come frightfully to mind. Kingman has finally gotten too sick to need me. Bad enough, but the other is worse.

They've found a new donor.

JULY 24

Finally. Early this morning, pitch black outside, the phone rang. It triggered a dream and I reached out to Claire with my phantom limb. She murmured something and nestled into my empty socket. I picked up the receiver.

His voice was urgent, lacking its familiar polish and restraint. He demanded to see me immediately, insisting that I meet him at his apartment. I agreed, but when I asked what was the matter, the phone was already dead.

Outside, the fog had settled to ground level, as thick as if it had sprung from the earth itself. Kingman's building was all but invisible from the street, the tall Greek columns seemingly anchored to clouds. A night clerk let me in, saying that Mr. Ho was expecting me. I wiped the moisture from my face and hair and entered the elevator. At the eighth floor I started to exit when Kingman suddenly appeared, shoving me back inside. He pulled the gate shut, hit the down button, then stopped the elevator between floors.

"The records," he said, facing me with wild, blood-shot eyes. "Where are the records?"

I searched my mind for some previous mention of records. Something to orient me. But he did not wait for a reply.

"I need to know what they're doing. All of them. Earnest faces, yes, but none as honest as they pretend. I've tried to get messages out. It's some game, isn't it? Some imposter's ploy . . ."

"Game? I don't understand."

"Why are they giving me four pills at night and only three in the morning? Tell me that, if you can."

"Four? Three?"

"It's a charade, isn't it? An imitation." He grinned,

as though pleased with himself, but the look was quickly gone. "It moves on channels beyond what the others can detect. It's lost to them, but not to us. Tell me, who are the higher authorities? Who pulls the strings?

"I'm asking for your help," he said, more urgently now. "Tell me what to do. I hear them talk. Even behind my back, it's obvious what they're saying. But I will not be discouraged.

"They couldn't do this to an ordinary man. I see it, and I am above it. When I will it to stop, it will stop. Do you understand? It is my duty."

His voice was high-pitched, his manner desperate. He paced frantically, careful not to touch me. All at once he stopped.

"Can you smell the decay? Even a strong person can't hold out forever. I need answers. Help me."

The man was clearly out of his mind, and I worried that the tiny space we were in was making him worse. I inched over to the elevator's control panel, eyeing the switch that would set us in motion, but as soon as I got close, he blocked my way. With a menacing look he leaned against the panel, bracing himself with both feet planted firmly on the floor. He placed his palms together in an attitude either of prayer or of warning and shut his eyes.

For the first time I got a good look at him. His hair was disheveled, his face mottled and red. His skin was marked by scores of tiny capillaries, many of which had burst. At one side of his neck, peeking above his shirt collar, was the edge of a recent skin graft. It was swollen and purple, with a crust that oozed yellowish liquid. I felt an urge to run, which was impossible, but also to comfort him. He seemed in furious pain, and had now put himself in a position of no escape. But when I stepped forward in an effort to help him, he opened his eyes and growled at me. I tried some words to calm him, but he only laughed, accusing me of trying to control him with my voice.

"I see what you're thinking," he said. "Trying to trick me with your deep tones. Don't you see that I'm your reflection? This is no joke."

He started humming to himself, a hysterical tune of his own making. Suddenly, the elevator began to move. His head darted frantically from side to side, and he slapped at the control switch and buttons. To no avail. Inexorably the car ascended, and at the eighth floor the blue-suited man was there to pull back the gate. Beside him, in slippers and bathrobe, stood Devora. The sight of her seemed to take something out of Kingman, who, having backed into a corner, let out a shuddering sigh and collapsed against the elevator wall.

We carried him into the apartment, and twenty minutes later Devora returned to tell me everything was all right.

"I must apologize for my husband's behavior." She offered me a drink, which I readily accepted. "Some of these drugs have such terrible effects."

"I don't know which of us was more scared."

"Him, I imagine." She took her drink to the window. "He's not himself these days."

"I'm not surprised."

She stiffened. "The irony does not escape me. But no, he's not." She sighed. "I suppose it's a wonder that things don't change any faster than they do."

I had no reply and stared with her out of the window, the reflection of our faces seeming to float in the fog.

"Have you ever written a book, then thrown it out? Destroyed it because it wasn't what you knew you could create, what you wanted to?"

"A book changes in the writing," I told her. "And then later, after. It could always become something else, something to cherish."

"Do you fall in love with what you write?"

"I suppose. Of a kind. It's always a stormy affair."

"But when things go bad, when they go astray, you know what to do."

I shrugged, and then all at once I understood what she was asking. "Someday Kingman will die," I told her. "Then you'll find out for yourself."

"I know how I'll act," she said quietly, as if she'd already planned it out. She seemed grateful to be able to tell me. "Is that shameful?"

"It's too early in the morning for shame."

"Yes." She touched a necklace and turned. "Do you find me attractive?"

I worked on my drink. She watched me and waited.

"You know the answer," I said at length. "You wouldn't have asked if you didn't."

"Vanity is such a scourge," she said with a self-deprecating little laugh.

I examined myself, my missing arm, toes and the rest.

"Isn't it."

JULY 28

Tonight, after I read him a bedtime story, Nick grabbed on to my arm and wouldn't let go. After a few minutes I asked him to stop, but he held on tighter.

"You have to stay," he said.

"Nickie, it's bedtime."

"I won't let you go."

"Three minutes," I said, relenting. "And then you sleep."

"You count."

The minutes passed, and when the time was up, Nickie still wouldn't let go.

"You have to leave your hand with me," he said.

"I've only got one left," I answered jokingly, touched by his possessiveness.

"Promise you won't take it away."

"I'm right next door, Nickie. I'm not going anywhere."

"Promise."

"I'm your father," I said. "You can't lose me." Gently, I pulled my arm away. "I love you, Nickie. I promise."

JULY 30

Claire and I naked in bed, her fingers working my back. One vertebra at a time, outlining each bone and muscle. I savor her touch, though I can't help wondering if she is taking inventory. When she reached the nub at the bottom of my spine, the little upturning before it dives between the buttocks, she stops. I make sounds to indicate that she should continue, but she is still. Then she starts to talk.

"When I was a kid, there was a boy. Joe something. He was older than me, with big buck teeth. Always popping his gum and showing his teeth. He used to get me in corners and rub up against me. Front to back, front to front if I didn't turn around fast enough. It was awful."

"You just remembered?"

"Joe something." Absently she touches me where she'd left off. "He had a tail."

"What?"

"A little tail. I didn't find out until later, after he had an operation to get rid of it. I was so happy when I heard."

"Why happy?"

"It seemed fair. Making me suffer like that, he should suffer too. I felt better just knowing that he'd suffered."

"Is this some message, Claire? A parable?"

"It's true."

"What's true?"

She traces the scar on my flank, taking her time. "Would it have been different if Nickie hadn't lost his leg? I'd still be working, you still troubled and angry. Things balance out. There's a funny kind of logic to all this."

"We have money."

"I'm happy for that. But something else."

"I'm dense tonight, Claire. What's on your mind?"

"I don't know." She touches the nub at the bottom of my spine, rubbing it as if to conjure the proper explanation. "It has to do with self-respect. Knowing the measure of things. The limits.

"You can stop whenever you want, Matt. This is not for money, it's not for me or Nickie. You must know that."

"I have inklings."

"Will you stop?"

"When I'm done. Yes. I promise."

AUGUST 8

My face is bandaged so that only my mouth and nostrils are in contact with the air. Sometimes I think I am being reduced to the point that nothing will remain of me but holes. Mercifully, I am heavily drugged.

This last operation was a tough one, and it was complicated by an infection. I write this by Dictaphone, which someone, Claire probably, has left by the pillow. Kingman developed a sudden, overwhelming necrosis of his face, a result of one of the drugs he's on. The skin from forehead to chin, ear to ear sloughed off en masse. I was called in an emergency, and when I saw how he looked, the pain and fear in his eyes, I knew I would not refuse. So they brought me in and took my own face.

I am glad my eye is covered, because there are things I'd just as soon not see. Claire's look of woe,

Nick's accusation and fear. I hear it well enough in their voices.

Tony called today, and while someone held the phone, he jabbered on excitedly about an offer from one of the big houses. Not much money, but an option clause that promises a lot if I deliver a second book within a year. So much has happened these last months that I had to ask him the name of the book they want to buy. He laughed and told me, then asked if I thought I could write another so soon. It was my turn to laugh, a feeble sound that barely escaped my lips.

"It's nearly done."

"The diary?" he asked. I must have mentioned it to him in a distant past. "You see it as a book?"

"Not that. The man. It's creation itself. Imagine, after all these years. You pray for success, you search in vain for the door only to realize you've already walked through."

Someone is holding my hand. Claire, I think, though it might be Devora. Heavy sedation makes my senses less than keen. Kingman has had a stroke. A massive one, and now his brain is dead. The news has the recurring and obsessive feel of a dream, yet all the substance and plausibility of reality.

His brain is dead.

A work of art must breathe life.

There seems only one thing left to do.

GRIEF

Rebecca Brown

WE'RE ALL AT THE AIRPORT to see our friend off to a foreign country none of us has been to before. Tonight there are hundreds of us. We all pitched in to buy the ticket. We bought her travel guides and sent her to Berlitz school. We traded evenings reading to her from phrase books and flash cards. We bought her luggage and clothes. We got letters of reference from well-connected people at home. We booked reservations for her in reliable hotels. We showed her our support. Though we're all reluctant to admit it, we live vicariously through her.

How did we choose her? Well, we didn't really. Like greatness, it was thrust upon her. The dubious honor of bringing us all together through our fear of departure.

Because beneath our party spirit, there's an edge. One thing's not arranged: her ticket home.

She stands at the gate to board the plane and we strain, from our distance at the end of the wide-open hall behind the electronic surveillance gate, to see her face. She turns to wave goodbye to all of us and I have a flash of vision: I recognize this as a photograph we will show each other in the future when we remember her. I expect to hear a camera click, but I don't. Everything is quiet. None of us even breathes. She turns to walk into the collapsible corridor that leads to the plane when I notice she's the only person boarding the flight. It's then, and only then, I realize she's actually leaving. She throws her shoulders back with confidence. Her golden hair swings with her gait. When I hear something, it is the sound of her skirt rustling in air.

After we return home, only the bravest of us will allow herself to think we might not get postcards from her. We were so conscientious to give her all our addresses. Someone even gave her a telephone calling card. However, not even the bravest of us will admit what we think is true.

In the first few weeks she is gone, we tell ourselves she's too excited and busy to get in touch. She's having fun, we tell ourselves. We elaborate beautiful fantasies of the sunny streets she walks through, the sculpted gardens she spends her afternoons in, the exquisite dishes she dines on every warm exotic evening. We people her life with people we want to love us. Every dream we have we give to her. Some of us even envy her, so convinced we are that she has what we want.

But in fact, we hear nothing from her at all.

Gradually, we think the same thing about her. We deal with this nobly, or rather, we deal with it with manners. It is one of the great, sad, tragic things that make us who we are. Our references to her grow vague, then disappear. We manage this transition without a word. But at home, alone, we each work hard at our forgetting. Here's what we forget:

We forget her hair. We forget the way it shone in the sun on the beach where we played in the summer. We forget the way she wore anklets and made us all laugh at her imitation of cartoon characters from our youth. We forget her milk-white complexion and the soft strong veins in her hands. We forget the dusty line of fuzz that covered the small of her back. We forget her small breasts inside her swimsuit. We forget the way her calves tightened when she crouched at the start of the city parks race. We forget the stories she told of her zany brother in the farm country. We forget the colored strips of cellophane she decorated her bedroom windows with so we could see the light make rainbows in the morning. We forget the warmth of her palms, the moisture of her hairline when she came home from a run. We forget the secret places she knew of when we were bored and couldn't think of anything to do. We forget the way she ordered sweet-and-sour pork and always, *always*, picked out the pork and only ate the sauce and vegetables. We forget the way she pushed back her hair from her forehead when she was trying to make a point. We forget her favorite song from her childhood. We forget the favorite shells she had collected from the northern shore when she went there with her family when she was eleven. We forget her annoying habit of never putting the toothpaste cap back on all the way and being obsessive about dust in her study. We forget her inability to compromise when her favorite program was on at the same time as a great movie. We forget the way she covered her mouth whenever she told a story she liked too much.

We forget in order to be happy.

That is why her lover, who forgets most of all of us, is happiest. She forgets things we never knew that, even if she wanted to, she couldn't tell us.

When most of the forgetting is done, something happens.

I get a call from her lover.

"I heard from her," she tells me. "She called me."

I can't say, "But that's impossible," without implying what we all think but don't say. Instead I say, "Oh, we'll have to hear about it."

I call several of us and say, "Her lover told me she heard from her. She thinks she got a phone call."

We agree it's a wrong number, a similar voice, even a cruel joke. We agree we don't need to do anything. Soon, we reason, her lover will forget the phone call.

But she calls me again. "I got another phone

call from her. She says she's doing fine, but she misses us."

I call a meeting.

"She hasn't forgotten the phone call," I say. "She says she's had another one."

"How do we know she didn't get a call?" someone asks.

We all turn. "That's impossible. It's imagination, just something she wants."

We decide to do something.

But we don't act fast enough. Her lover shows us a postcard she says she sent which says that she'll be home. The handwriting is faint and shaky. We must help our poor foolish sister through her grief by exposing her fantasy for what it is. So we pretend to agree with her in her expectation when she goes to the airport to meet the return flight. We all know she will not come back. We are not surprised when she does not arrive at the airport. But our poor, foolish sister is insistent. "She missed the flight," she tells us. "She'll be here." We go again. Again she isn't there. Again she says she missed the flight but will come back. We go again. Soon we go there all the time, forgetting we're only there to keep our poor sister company. Instead, we start thinking like her; we think she will return.

We show ourselves in huge numbers at the airport. We tell ourselves there's power in numbers. Even though we know we simply haven't got any power when it comes to this. We start reenacting the past, hoping our re-creating can undo it. Over and over we relive her final days with us, her departing flight. We stand where we were, we shout as we did. We try to do what we hadn't done then. The truth is, we never wanted her to go. We were afraid.

The past comes back to us, vivid as blood, how we tried to soothe ourselves with final comforts. But all we did was give her guidebooks and feed her her favorite home-cooked meal the night before she left, throw her a farewell party. We vowed undying love and meant it, but learned that what we needed was forgetfulness, the only release from sorrow there is. And even now there is nothing we can do about our grief.

We stayed with her in vigils before she left. We told her we'd change places with her if we could; we couldn't. All our good intentions profited neither us nor her anything. All we could do was pretend—while she was with us—that she was coming back.

That's why we go to the airport in our party clothes. Why we sing "Welcome Home" as we remember pushing her toward her flight, why the cake we decorated says "Welcome Back," why we refuse to sublet her room, why we refuse to offer help to her lover because we don't want to imply that she needs help, why we've left the bon voyage decorations up, the pink and yellow streamers, the cheery opaque balloons on the ceiling, the color-coordinated plastic forks and spoons, why we laugh and tell ourselves we're so clever to recycle them into Welcome Home.

We wander from gate to gate all the time. We stand and watch as flights deplane and people kiss their loved ones home. We mill around wearing our party hats and blowing our party favors. We offer punch and cookies to reunited couples, families, friends. "Welcome Home! Welcome Home!" we cry, knowing the next flight will bring her back to us.

With our practiced songs and our party clothes, we make people happy. Especially her lover, because she is the most beautiful. She drapes her tan healthy body with light spring clothes, her arms and legs firm like a gorgeous young animal. In her bright green and blue and yellow silks, she smiles gracefully, but with the expectation of a confident child. Her longing for her lover's return, her nostalgia for every warm inch of her lover's flesh, is so strong we are almost afraid to be near her. She is flushed with the beauty of things about to happen. Her full, just parted lips, are ready.

We are sure she cannot have left us, sure she'll be back, sure she'll return even stronger and more beautiful than when she left. She will have braved something marvelous and strange. We are sure she'll enter with a flourish and tell us we were wrong to have remembered and forgotten what we did, to have ever stopped believing she'd come back.

291

*

But tonight, that's almost all I know, that I have stopped believing. It's not something anyone notices; my party hat is still on straight and my full lace skirt is crisp as starch. But I am singing our happy "Welcome Home" with only part of me. I imagine the sagging points of party hats, damp limp paper horns, ice cream turning to foamy puddles on paper plates, crumbs of lemon layer cake ground into the cracks between the linoleum tiles. Maybe the flush is weariness, not excitement.

In fact, I think I never believed that she'd come back. But I knew I needed something. I wanted to find it in all of us. I was warmed by our costumes and camaraderie, our routines of ritual comfort. And, truly, I love the songs we sing together and the sweet look on people's faces at the airport when we give them cake and tell them about our friend.

But I didn't do these things because I thought she would return. I did them for us. And I did them in case, somehow, she could know. I did them to tell her that I would remember her. I did them to tell her goodbye.

The last memory I have of you, you're falling. Alone in the airplane corridor, you stumble. Your thin shoulders are hunched as though you're being pushed down. You can't bear to turn and look at us on your way out because you know what we'll see in your hopeless face.

The sound is your final gasp of air before you could tell us goodbye.

DEAR DEAD PERSON

Benjamin Weissman

1

IN TONIGHT'S SHOW, contrary to our better judgment we bring you the old-fashioned fable of *an unendurable man* known only as (raises his arm), who wakes up one morning, vomits, and looks in the mirror to discover a face as despicable and repellent as a moldy block of cheese, a smooth yet unshaven face, which radiates a frightful bitterness, *malignant, demoralized, hysterical*—with narrow unappealing lips, pale and unkissable; *God damn I'm ugly* . . . In the classic American tradition of *following one's own drummer* he sets out on a mission to destroy everything around him, starting with what's inside his apartment: the smashing of each lightbulb and spotty window; the throwing of two wind-up clocks, numerous silly books, wooden folding chairs, the framed family portrait, shoes, tomatoes, a honeydew melon, figs (which really opens up a psychic *can of worms*); the squashing of the goldfish; he lights the cat on fire; kicks the dog to death; shoots his daughter and son; strangles his wife and heaves their newborn infant against the wall; *clutter*, he screams, *every person takes up so much room*; to calm his nerves he masturbates into a shot glass and downs his semen; after he disembowels the family he breaks into an old lady's apartment, ties her up, defecates, and spoon-feeds her the stools, *my body's liberation*, he says, *is your midnight snack*; he masturbates a second time into the feces-covered face of the woman; laughter overtakes him and during this time he feels better than he's ever felt before; he wipes the tip of his genital with a surprisingly useful doily, *I'm finally doing what I want to do and I'm great at it*; he is exhilarated, close to tears, wildly in love with life, a child of sorts, *I'm the only person in the world able to do all this, I am irreplaceable, I am great, I am who everyone wants to be*; he falls asleep and dreams he is on vacation; he steps onto the terrace of a hotel to observe the ocean; he sees a marlin burst out of the water, fly over the sand, and dive into the hotel pool; *the ocean is so exciting*, he thinks, *so big, so majestic*, he shakes his head, *I like a fish with a dagger on its face*; the marlin jumps out of the pool and pierces a bikini-clad gentleman in the stomach; the unfortunate man and fish fall to the ground; he is happy as he watches blood gush out of the man; he wakes up, masturbates a third time and sets the entire neighborhood on fire with a flame-thrower he saved from the war; *the world is passive*, he says as smoke rises all around him, *I am the active one, the spring rain of contempt, a swift morose icon, my gift is misguided love, I'm the only person who's truly supposed to be here.*

2

Our birthday boy is burning his T-shirt and sneakers and hair with my best box of wooden matches. He pretends he hasn't done anything. I see the damage. I smell the sulfur. He's not going to get away with it, not my boy, birthday or no birthday. A boy should be thankful for being allowed to live another year, this one's nine, a devil in prepubescent clothing. No one should disrespect the gifts of Earth. That's a flat rule. I snack on several doughnuts and a bowl of chili and discover six pennies missing from my dresser. This is all in one day, the clock hasn't struck noon yet. Something's got to be done, something firm and unforgettable. Punishments are unavoidably wicked. So I call the criminal forth and he denies all charges. But I am the judge. I tap knuckles on my gam and whisper, guilty, justice must prevail, and sentence the pyro-thief to a paddling. I grab my trusty broken broom handle, and the naughty boy runs around the apartment screaming; but he can't escape, the back door is deadbolted. I waddle as fast as I can, whacking him a few times to tame him. I get him into position in the family room. Each swat only makes him wilder.

What's a two-hundred-pound mother to do? Here's what I do: I toss the stick down and flip the creature on his back and sit on his chest. I shove an unsavory sock into his mouth to cut the volume, pick up a *TV Guide*, see what's on tonight and this week. I become engrossed in a witty article about some new trends, and then a very important exposé about the hypocrisy of beauty pageants. Then my other little offspring comes fluttering in and demands I get off her brother. I say, who do you think you are? Who do you think you're talking to? Do you want to be next? She says, Mom, you're hurting him, he's not breathing, he's blue, he's not alive. And she pushes me. She defies her mother. Then she picks up the phone and starts dialing, looking at the emergency numbers I conscientiously taped to the phone. I say, put that receiver down right this second. She whispers, please help me, my mother is killing my brother, our address is 250 Heliotrope, I'm his sister, please come quick. She doesn't hang up. Very nice performance, little lady. No allowance for you. No dinner for you. You are grounded. She presses the receiver to her chest and starts sobbing. I've gotten so comfortable I can't rise off our birthday boy to slap the nonsense out of the brat.

3

Favorite parts—I save them, I love them (torso, head). I throw the rest away (feet, legs, arms), I hate them (toes, too). But I love elbows. It's unsettling how elbows are pointy one minute and squishy and flaccid the next. No different than myself, or any man for that matter. I pinch my own elbow when I feel tense. I do it all day long.

A person never truly appreciates a head until they see it separated, by itself, on a stick, or held in your hands. You nuzzle it. You twist the ear and no one shouts. A thing that once screamed so loud is now a perfection in pieces, my silent ecstasy.

I address the head. I start an argument, lose my patience and sling it across the room. The head thumps against the wall and plops to the ground in a mute sort of way, more like a sandbag. Human flesh hitting a hard wood floor is a recognizable sound. I'd call it classical.

This morning, at a cost of $24.00, marked down from $29.00, I purchased a red valise. Is that an obvious color? The head and torso fit neatly inside. I've never gotten over the fact that vinyl is such a superior material. Inexpensive, looks like leather, and any stain wipes right off.

I close the lid. My joy is gone. It disappears the way the world blackens when I shut my eyes. So quick and cold. The fuzzy shapes remain in my warm brain. With my nasal congestion I'm unable to smell what I trust to be supremely aromatic, the decomposing boy.

Wednesday nights are trash nights. Skunks come down from the mountains and waddle through the neighborhood garbage. That's my second favorite smell. Skunks. They're so wonderful, so slow and vulnerable. A tiny face and a big flirty ass. Doesn't that make sense in a funny way, a stinky animal picks at stinky food? For the record—since I'm here to tell all—other unpopular smells close in the running: cheese, gasoline, sulfur, my armpits, my farts. When I fart (my farts are brilliant) I see a stranger in my basement—he is moaning, but not unhappy.

I open the valise. The boy is still with me. God bless him, even if he wasn't a good boy. God bless me. I know better.

I lift the head from the valise. By itself it weighs as much as a small baby. You are so much trouble. I step out of my underwear and play with the head. I bounce it against my pimply butt: *boing boing.* I've never been able to keep my butt free of blemishes. I feel silly applying teenage medicine back there at my age, but

300   I do it anyway. I make the effort. I plant the boy's face up my ass, his naughty little pug nose Eskimo kisses my repulsive hole. I try to fart. Nothing. I feel a shit inside but unfortunately it's too far up to come out.

From the mirror on the wall I can tell you that my asshole looks just like anyone else's. Shall we say like a corrupt belly button? No better, no worse. It's just there, pinched and inscrutable. And that means I'm here—living and breathing. Some people pinch themselves. It's a good thing to do. Check and see if you're still here. If I'm still here.

I bring the head around to my belly and rub my cock against the bridge of his nose. Such patience. Thank you. I push myself into his stubborn mouth and fuck the gray face. I need a new watchband. I've had this one six months. They should last longer than that. I pull out all the way to see myself—hello there—

and then all the way back in, as deep as I can. I twirl the head around like a slow pinwheel. When was the last time he brushed those teeth? I know it's been at least two days. Teeth feel good. I like it when it hurts. Yes. Just like that. Uh huh. Oh you little fuck head, you dead little shit, you can't do this to me, my god. And when I've suffered as much pain as I can stand I pull out and squirt on your eyelids.

Killing, cutting up boys has made me a better person. It took me so long to notice. Now when I give, I expect nothing in return.

4

When the circus comes to town you have to be prepared for fun. So many good things happen near the big top. The sad clowns come out and play. They're so silly. Even though I flunked clown college I'm still a clown. I can't even eat a sandwich without spilling jelly down my front. But when the show's over the clown leaves his red nose on and gets fucked up on booze. Then he goes berserk. He plays again, all by his little lonesome. But this time none of the children laugh and the stupid fat parents aren't bored anymore, especially after I, or after he, pulls the trigger of the squirt gun and, wow, drills metal into your sweetbreads. Is that a warm thought, I mean feeling? Don't you feel giddy? I know I do. Then the off-duty clown cuts you down to size with the goofiest hatchet and boils your bones—maybe I'm a witch, maybe I'm amazed—for a rude smelly soup, and throw the parts he doesn't like away into an irrigation ditch. Can't run very fast, oops, not with these big floppy shoes.

People among us live to cut off heads. I fuck to cut them up and shit Hail Mary. I cum all over myself in the hope that your head rolls down the street. I spray a load in the dirt. The fertilizer of tomorrow. Jack-off techniques have gone downhill. Accuracy and distance are an embarrassment. Clown fuck badly. Roll around in the mud with the sprinklers clicking over my head. Clown fuck funny: aims for the eyes, only dribbles on cheeks. Clown fuck sadly, cum like teardrops.

5

Most people's lives are drab and uneventful. They enjoy the excitement of an accident. It gives them something to talk about and makes them feel important because they were there. Then of course, there's morbid curiosity. It is one of the less attractive qualities of human nature, but we all have it in varying degrees.

—Ann Landers

Dear Dead Person:
I just wanted to write you a little note to say how happy you made my family and me. We were on our way home from a short vacation to the lake— the kids, in the backseat, sunburned from head to toe, complained about this and that: how much longer till we get home, they were starving as usual (so was I in fact), and my wife, Sam, was losing her temper—a slap to someone's face from one of

her two quick hands was imminent. All of a sudden
the traffic brought us to a stop. Your accident was
up ahead. At first we didn't know what it was—I
thought, it's probably no big deal, just a small wreck,
a dinky fender bender. About a mile ahead I
noticed a distinct swirl of blackish smoke poofing
into the air. A good sign, I thought. Twenty minutes
later, everyone's patience tested to the max, our car
crept up to the scene. What a joy it was, and well
worth the wait. A person rarely gets to see such a
sight.

My kids were adorable. They continued to yell and
scream, but very intelligently I thought. My son,
Eric, requested I turn down the radio. I recall I had
it on an oldies station. I turned the damn thing off.   303

"Dad," Eric said (the boy is seven), "wouldn't it be
neat to make cars that were smashed up like that
one to begin with, then when the car crashed it
wouldn't look damaged. Or maybe someone could
design cars that looked upside down."

I think the boy could market that idea, I do. "That
someone is you, Eric," I said.

My daughter, Nina, admired the way the firemen
walked—big methodical steps. Sam asked me if the
sheets they put over the dead were made specially
for that purpose. I didn't know, so I just said yes.

The family came alive as I've never seen before.
Sam yodeled in fits of happiness. She reached for
my hand and squeezed it. Then she slid over, grabbed
the back of my neck, and kissed me roughly on the
mouth. Wow. Then she gave me an infinitely

powerful look with her big browns. I love that woman.

I often wonder what it is that kids enjoy today, and I haven't the faintest idea. What with the video games, the strange movies in sequel, their private undecipherable slang, who can keep up? Here was something we could all appreciate. A current event; or a tragedy if you will . . . depending on how you see it, of course.

"I count six bodies, Daddy," Eric noted.

"Look at that naked man," Nina said, "he's bright red with little black specks."

I slowed down. That was you. I stopped the car. You must've been alive at the time even though that seemed impossible. Your left leg flinched. Today's paper reported that you died once you arrived at the hospital. Your torn-up legs were bent in such an abnormal pose. You looked like one of Nina's dolls after Eric has inducted it into his army. I'm really sorry. I assumed every bone in your body was broken. One fluid action causing all that damage.

I expected the car behind me to honk. But I looked in the rearview and they were just as engrossed as we were.

Eric crawled halfway out the back window before Sam reeled him in. "Please Mommy," he said, "I want to touch the dead people."

"Listen Eric," I said, "we are here and that's the important thing. Appreciate this moment from where you are, be grateful you can see this much, and anyway, son, the police won't allow you to touch the dead, you have to be a member of the family to get that privilege."

"But that's not fair," he said.

"Okay, that's enough," I said.

Clearly, it was time for us to move on. And so we did. I just want to say, for myself, the best part of the experience, if I may be so bold, was your face. It wasn't a face. Just raw living meat. Do you know what astonishes me? Take away one layer of our skin and suddenly we look like monsters.

Respectfully yours,

MAN OF IMPORTANCE

ARMED RESPONSE

Ann Rower

I WALKED INTO the Family Room. Joey's on the phone but he blows me a kiss. Shirlie loves the phone too. Her mother Rose, my stepmother for a few short years—got an Oscar for the best phone performance. In LA it's like talking on the phone is always performance art. At home, I like privacy for my calls, no matter who I'm talking to, but out there it's like they make you sit there and listen to them talk on the phone. You walk into someone's house out there and you haven't seen them in six months and they don't hang up. He can't. He's holding, waiting to talk to someone at CalGas. It hasn't rained in so long they fine you if you use too much water so Shirlie and Joey and all good SoCals were really trying now. They were forced to cut water back 10% this month and then if it didn't rain, 25% percent in May and if it was still dry, 50% by June. Life without pool, sprinkler, car wash. It was so unthinkable. But both he and Shirlie had been very careful.

Shirlie, my stepsister ever since my father, Lester, who wrote a lot of very famous screenplays married her mother, Rose, a few years ago. Both were in their eighties and both are now dead but Shirlie is still my new but forever as she would say stepsister and I love her a lot. When I come in she is sitting on the floor cutting up Candee's copy of Lester's Trust file, which divided Lester's classic hit movies royalties among our family (Lester's sister Berdie, Rodie, me—because my mother had died, and the Trust stipulated that the offspring became beneficiaries—Gus, because Ruthie, Lester's littlest sister had died and the Trust stipulated that the money would pass to the husbands; even Jessie, who was Lester's brother Nate's paramour for forty years though not his legal spouse was named as Nate's successor in the Trust documents which went into effect only after Rose died) and Rose's family (her daughter Shirlie—tho not Shirlie's husband Joey, for some strange reason which no one will ever know because the dead, even screenwriters, tell no tales,— but of course Shirlie and Joey's kids, their sons, Lance, and Chris, and Candee, their daughter) into littler and littler pieces, crying as she gets up to greet me.

It's so sad, Shirlie says. Just when Candee'd gotten a little money for extras . . . Her teacher's salary was so small, that little school in the valley, she sobs then smiles, as Grizzy plays with the shredded documents. Grizzy's Candee's cat. She's named for Grizzabella, from *Cats*. Candee was an avid Andrew Lloyd Webber fan.

Why don't you burn them, I say.

It's because of the drought. You can burn cloth but not paper. I know because we burned our flag.

They had a flag out too, for the war, but Joey made her take it down when the Gulf War was officially over. She said they drug out their old flag to put up at first but it was all torn and old and so they bought a new flag. But before they put it up she looked up in an etiquette book about how to dispose of an old flag which said the only way was to burn it. So they cut it up in little pieces and burned it in the fireplace, feeling it was a risk because you're not allowed to burn paper if you live in the hills but cloth is not paper though she had to spend a day on the phone checking to see if it was okay. I thought it was interesting that the proper way to dispose of a flag is the same act as the crime. Remember when Bush's main domestic policy was to try to get the Supreme Court to make flag burning a capitol offense and all the artists protested?

She had to have her automatic garbage Disposall and her dishwasher hooked up with a special new attach-

ment you can buy—it took them three Thursdays—
Joey's day off—driving around from Downtown LA
to Santa Monica to find one—which shunts the water
from the disposal into the dishwasher—yuk I mean
the other way around—so you don't waste it—I think
there's a name for that now—graywater—She's really
trying. Her consciousness had been elevated consider-
ably since the last time I was out when she thought the
Greenhouse Effect was a kitchen window treatment.

Eat shit says Joey by way of greeting. He clicks the
little pocket XXX voice sampler his sons gave him
for Christmas again and smiles. Fuck you. You're an
asshole.

Let's eat, Joey says. Where are we going for lunch?
310 What do you feel like eating he says to me.

What are my options, I say. We go through this
routine before every meal so I know.

Hamlet Gardens or Ivy at the Beach.

Joey, says Shirlie emphatically. We can't go to the
beach. We have to go to Westwood Boulevard to
the bulb place to find a certain kind of light bulb that's
called hollagen.

It's pronounced halogen. You make it sound like
collagen, I said.

No says Joey, laughing, that's what you put on your
titties.

No I say That's silicone. You put collagen on your
lips. Silicone Valley, I laugh. Nobody gets it.

I love the Hamlet.

Not Hamburger Hamlet.

I know, Hamlet Gardens. In Westwood. I used to

go there with Aunt Rose. I heard the Hamlets all went out of Business except Kate Mantilini.

They did but they're still there. They're just not the same.

Or Nate and Al's.

I get up to go out the front door.

Oh, no, Shirlie says. This way.

She points to the bathroom off the family room and slides the door open fast.

Hurry.

I slip through following her, flashing on Joey opening the door once while I was changing into my bathing suit flushing deep purple mutters something like don't they have locks on the doors in New York? which didn't strike me at the time but now of course I realize that in a sense, they, we, don't. I heard that now in LA whenever a building is being planned they hire a cop as well as an architect to advise on security. I wonder if he remembers. I remember I was bending down to stick my foot into the suit and my tits must have been hanging like, well, globes I hope. Does he remember? (of course) What did he see? (everything)—all slip through my mind as I close the door from the family room into the bathroom and Shirlie slides opens the second bathroom door from the bathroom to the service entrance.

Beep beep service door opening. Reset beep beep.

Come.

Beep. Beep. Garage door opening. Reset.

The only way you can get out of the house now is to go out the garage door (which is a three door

311

operation) rather than the front door making sure you can first slide the bathroom door closed before you open the service garage door. As soon as the talking armed response security system says Service garage door opens Reset, you hurry out so the alarm doesn't go off while Joey quickly raises the garage door and you hurry out there and he resets the alarm then gets into his car and pulls out and you get in and he closed the garage door from the car so there's no way Grizzy, Candee's cat, can get out. It's a new LA phobia. Fear of something bad happening to somebody else. Shirlie's panic is that something will happen to the Grizzabella, the cat.

If anything ever happened to her I'd kill myself, she once slipped.

Joey has it about Shirlie. That's why Joey got her the car phone. Joey bought Shirlie a car phone. It was a present. To use in emergencies. Only in emergencies. So he didn't tell her the number.

Till I came along, everyone in my side of the family called him a monster. He calls everyone an animal. Marta is the animal. All people of color are animals. He makes jokes about Italian waiters and Mexican cooks, about queer people and poor people. He's a mean man, a rigid man, a hard man but he turns me on. He looks good. His hair is red gold and shining in the sunlight.

You gotta new car, I say.

Yeah, he says, fishing around in the pocket of his

actually old leather bomber jacket for his car keys. I used to get a new car every time I got depressed. This was a three car year.

It's a mother—a mother of pearl colored Allante Caddy. It's a convertible.

I recall they recalled them a few years back, I say.

He says Oh really? He says he traded his old Mercedes in for this American car. First American car he ever had since he was seventeen. He says he really wanted the white Merc convertible but it was 70 thou and his Caddy lists for only fifty eight. He got it for 34. His licence plate says UPPAUSA. The USA makes me thinks its some kind of patriotic statement. Everybody's very patriotic, it being just after the Gulf War thang, and, incidentally, the exact day after a motorist name Rodney King was, much to Joey's delight, beaten by a bunch of LA cops. Shirlie's not that patriotic but she does adore ribbons and she has tied yellow ribbons around everything but Joey's dick: her little mailbox which is a miniature of the big locked house, the wine bottles in the cuvenet; even tied them around the ARMED RESPONSE signs. I read in the paper how someone in the neighborhood who was a member of the California Peace Movement refused to tie any ribbons to anything and so someone came by and sprayed yellow paint all over his new Silver Jetta. I look back at Joey's licence plate and read it again: UPPAUSA. Up your ass. Yesterday in Century City I saw a red Rolls Corniche convertible that said SHOCKER. A XJ12 that read IWANT69. The 1991 BMW 5251 next door says WE2RHOT. My cousin

313

Mark's Dodge Stealth R/T Turbo says GODFADA. There goes one: WUVUMUC. The last wuz a little red Mazda Miata. Musta been an anniversary present. It's not Orwell's newspeak exactly or a maybe combo of that and Hallmark card but it's a whole other kind of language you have to learn out here in order to read the customized license plate which I guess they have so they can tell one Mercedes from another.

I fantasize if I had one I'd call them Sadies but Joey calls them Mercs, like with a "k."

Joey sticks his hand in his pocket and squeezes.

Suck my dick!

314   He makes himself laugh with that thing but since his car only seats two people when we got to lunch we take Shirlie's Mercedes. Her licence says SHIRLEEE, with 3 "e's," because the "ie" and "ee" were already taken.

At lunch—Hamlet Gardens—everybody cries, even Joey. He gave me some new details, like she didn't take pills she took insect poison. Actually she took pills then insect poison. Actually she called the night before and sounded slurry and Shirlie was worried and wanted to drive by but Joey said we'll go over in the morning. They did go over in the morning. They found Candee lying half in and half out of the bathroom face down, Grizzy sitting silently by the vomit which was half in and half out of Candee's mouth. He tried to block Shirlie's entrance, shoving her roughly back out to wait in her car until one of their sons, who Joey called, came but since any suicide is considered a suspicious death the police detained Joey for six hours because he'd found the note. He told me he would show me the note. I never saw a real live suicide note. I'm dying to see it.

I'm still pissed at Candee for "leaving" he said. He sent his Nicoise salad with fresh tuna back because the fish was too cooked, tan not pink. The second time he sent it back it was too raw. He wanted to order something else but the waitress practically got on her knees and begged him to let her bring him a third one. I thought it was so sexy, kinda. The third time it was perfect.

Coffee?

I'll have a double decaf espresso says Joey.

Shirlie says I'll have decaf regular coffee in the teensiest cup you have.

After the waitress leaves Shirlie explains to me that that way it stays hot. She explains that Candee got the idea of the insect poison from a Danielle Steel book.

I remember she was reading it the last time I came out, I said, sipping the foam off my cappiccino.

Shirlie told me the funny thing is that she paid for the poison by check and the check bounced but when the hardware store called and Shirlie told the man Candee had passed away he said don't worry about the check. He'd cover it himself. I didn't tell him she killed herself.

From that moment my ghoulishness took over. I had to see that note. But how do you ask? What words? Answer. None. Try body language. Raising your eyebrows? I looked like Groucho. Wiggling your lips? Marilyn. So for hours in the mirror I practice an expression which says you promised to show me your daughter's suicide note and I'm leaving in four days so please wont you get it out and let me read it but I couldn't get it right. It looked too much like fuck me.

Candee: 2 ee's. She had a name job, like they do. She was born CANDY, then changed it to CANDEE. Then after she failed to get that Taco Bell commercial, her agent suggested she change it to CANDYN because it sounded androgynous, like Jamie Lee Curtis. He even put his voice on her answering machine saying CANDYN is not home.

I was obsessed. I started searching for the note that first night when they were asleep. Where would he keep it? In the family room. In the memory room? In her old bedroom? I snuck downstairs at dawn and all of a sudden the alarm went off. The whole house is armed even the stairs. Not only is it armed. It talks.

It started saying front stairs beep beep front stairs occupied. Usually when I stay there they turn off the stairs but the first night they forgot. I raced back up and slipped under the covers just as I heard Marta come running out of her room and Shirlie and Joey bolt from their beds but I pretended I was asleep and pretended they'd blame Marta, or maybe Grizzy. I was so thrown though that I was afraid to open anything. I was trapped in a house with a talking security system and they didn't even think to give me an exit code— even Marta had an exit code—and I didn't know how to ask for one. I think they thought I would probably fuck it up and leave the house wide open or set off the alarm when I went out. I don't know what gave them that idea but I was embarrassed to ask them for an exit code so when I wanted to go for a walk I had to wait to be let out. I felt like a dog.

But it made me start thinking about codes, my feeling about using my mother's personal 4-digit code at the bank like those funny little poopy sounds as I touch the screen feels like I'm tapping into my mother. But a personal exit code is different. It's access not into but out of. I mean how many places set off alarms when you try to exit? I mean besides mental wards and prisons? I'm starting to think that all this increase in panic disorders, especially in LA is the counterside of all these security systems, all this ARMED RESPONSE. I distinctly remember the first time I saw those ARMED RESPONSE signs on the lawns in LA. Actually it was in the Valley. But I pictured houses full of people permanently hiding behind the long drapes they all have to keep the sun out,—the houses on the Valley are always so dark, except for the t.v. flicker—with guns in their hands at the ready and peeping out so if you try to break in they shoot you. I never imagined it meant being locked into a house so if someone comes to break in you can't get out. Maybe it has to do with all the practice you get with denial that must come from trying to get used to living on the fault line. There's no doubt in my mind panic disorders are on the increase and like so many things that start in LA—like NAIL places and sandwich girls—it's spreading east. Fear of

heights depths inside outside people, animals, cars, public, private. I mean I heard an ad on the car radio yesterday for a radiology place, maybe it was mammograms, specifically, but it ended saying and the best news is we have large airy open spaces to wait in, not those tiny dark cubicles, in case you're claustrophobic. Like it was the normal thing. And someone else told me that sky divers say that the more they do it, the more fearful they get. I notice that happening the more I do it, live, that is, too. I never used to mind anything but I notice that I like to keep the window cracked in the car now, even in the winter and my friend Marchel once said "is that a phobia?" I'd never thought of it before but he pinned me. It was a tiny little question but it somehow seemed like a major intimate moment. It must have been because he put it in one of his stories even though it was my phobia. I guess having your phobias exposed leaves you so vulnerable.

(To flash forward a mo: After the Rodney King decision I was afraid to call Shirlie because I thought Joey would answer and say something horrible about the "rioters." I wondered what they would do about their hard and fast schedule of eating out Saturdays what with the curfew but she said it was no problem. They went "up." (The restaurants on top of the canyon up Beverly Glen on Mulholland were allowed to stay open. No way the Bloods were gonna get that high up. The worst thing though was she said she was in the Beverly Center, of all places, when the riots spilled over that brief fabulous moment into Bev Hills. The Beverly Center is a vertical Mall with restaurants and Irvine Ranch (the greatest market west of Dean and Deluca) and California Pizza and valet parking on the ground floor and a 15-plex Odeon movie house on top and inbetween, chains—the Gap, Victoria Secret, Radio Shack—and two big LA departments stores, the Broadway, (like Macy's) and Bullocks, (like Saks, but in fact owned by Macy's). Anyway Shirlie was shopping in Bullocks when the riots started. When burning and looting on the ground floor started the management of Bullocks decided the safest thing would be to lock the doors from the inside. I tried to imagine all these probably claustrophobic West LA ladies locked into Bullocks trying to feel safe from some rampaging looter who must have been running around with a machine gun in one hand and a slice of pesto pizza with sun dried tomatoes and chevre in the other: like ARMED RESPONSE, totally.) But it just confirms my feelings that security, rather than eliminating it, creates fear.

No wonder Candee "decided to leave."

It was Joey, who I never talked to on the phone before in my whole life who called to tell me: he said

Hello Ann . . . It's Joey . . . Shirlie's all right . . . That's not why I'm calling . . . are you sitting down . . . Candee died, in one breath.

Before I hung up, I said I know you're not the hugging type but give Shirlie a hug for me.

He growled I hug you, don't I.

320   It was months after Candee's death before Shirlie would pick up the phone. Finally she sent her own note typed and xeroxed on gray marbled parchment paper:

to you who share in this feeling of loss, our
treasured memories of Candy are supposed to
help heal the sorrow. will they? It's so difficult now
to believe that they ever will. we were so close,
will there ever be a time when I can read a menu
and see iced gazpacho, oysters, scampi,
quesadillas, chocolate mousse pie, or
margaritas . . .

When I finally talked to Shirlie on the phone a month later she was okay for five minutes and then she broke down:

"She never went to New York," Shirlie sobbed.

"She'd never been to Europe. She'd never gone to see the changing of the leaves. . . . She never (sob) even got (sob) to see *Phantom* . . ."

DEAREST MOM, DAD, LANCE, CHRIS, LOREAN, MANDIE AND MORGAN,

USUALLY WRITING COMES PRETTY EASILY TO ME BUT THIS IS VERY DIFFICULT NOW BECAUSE I KNOW I AM GOING TO CAUSE THE PEOPLE I LOVE MOST IN THE WORLD GREAT PAIN. (TRY TO BE STRONG, MOM)

PLEASE TRY NOT TO BE ANGRY WITH ME FOR TAKING MY LIFE. DADA, I KNOW YOU THINK SUICIDE IS THE EASY WAY OUT, BUT *NO ONE* CAN TRULY UNDERSTAND THE DEPTHS OF DESPAIR I FEEL EXCEPT FOR ME. AND MAYBE IT IS THE EASIEST WAY OUT, BUT AS WILLIAM STYRON SAID, FOR THE *DEEPLY DEPRESSED* PERSON THEY SEE NO OTHER WAY BECAUSE THE PAIN IS SO DEEP THEY JUST WANT SOME RELIEF. AND THAT'S HOW I FEEL. I *CANNOT* TAKE ONE MORE DAY OF LIVING WITH MYSELF. I DON'T HAVE THE STRENGTH OR PATIENCE TO FIGHT ANYMORE. I AM SO WORN OUT. THIS IS NOT A WAY TO GET ATTENTION OR CRY OUT FORE MORE HELP. I *WANT* TO DIE. FOR A LOT OF REASONS.

I KNOW IT'S GOING TO BE HARD FOR YOU ALL TO ACCEPT, BUT PLEASE TRY AND UNDERSTAND THAT THIS IS WHAT I *WANT*. IT'S MY CHOICE. WE ALL MAKE OUR CHOICES IN LIFE EVEN IF IT SOMETIMES MEANS HURTING OTHERS. BUT PLEASE DON'T THINK OF ME AS BEING SELFISH.

AND MOM AND DAD, I WANT TO STRESS TO YOU NOT TO FEEL ANY GUILT. YOU WERE BOTH WONDERFUL PARENTS. I DIDN'T DESERVE TO HAVE SUCH GREAT PARENTS. AND IN MY EARLIER DAYS I DIDN'T ALWAYS TREAT YOU WITH ENOUGH OF THE RESPECT THAT IS SO OBVIOUS TO ME NOW THAT YOU WERE ALWAYS WORTHY OF. AND FOR THAT I APOLOGIZE TO YOU BOTH. BUT UNFORTUNATELY, FOR A GOOD DEAL OF MY LIFE I'VE BEEN AN UNHAPPY PERSON. AND I BELIEVE THAT IS JUST ME, PART OF MY MAKEUP—MY INATE PERSONALITY—AND SOMETHING I AM DOUBTFUL I CAN EVER REALLY CHANGE COMPLETELY. I CAN'T STAND THE THOUGHT OF LIVING OUT THE REST OF MY LIFE BEING UNHAPPY AND SUBJECT TO SUCH DEEP DEPRESSIONS (WHICH IS NOTHING NEW TO ME—I'VE ALWAYS HAD THEM THROUGHOUT MY LIFE) I'D RATHER NOT LIVE AT ALL.

I KNOW THIS IS GOING TO BE VERY HARD FOR MANDIE AND MORGAN TO GRASP BUT IT IS MY HOPE THAT ONE DAY WHEN THEY'RE OLDER THEY WILL UNDERSTAND MORE. AND PLEASE CONVEY TO THEM HOW VERY MUCH THEIR AUNT LOVED THEM, AND I PRAY THAT THEY WILL LIVE OUT HAPPY LIVES. MY BIGGEST REGRET IS NOT BEING ABLE TO WATCH THEM GROW UP INTO ADULTS. BY THE WAY, PLEASE MAKE SURE MY INHERITANCE MONEY GOES TO THEM FOR THEIR COLLEGE EDUCATIONS.

AS FAR AS GRIZABELLA IS CONCERNED, 323 PLEASE TRY AND SEE THAT SHE GOES TO A GOOD HOME. I WOULD LIKE IT IF SHE WENT WITH YOU, MOM AND DAD, TO LIVE BUT I KNOW YOU'RE NOT THRILLED WITH THE PROSPECT OF HAVING ANY MORE PETS, SO THAT MAY NOT BE POSSIBLE.

THE FOLLOWING IS A LIST OF PEOPLE I WOULD LIKE TO BE INVITED TO MY FUNERAL BESIDES FAMILY MEMBERS:

1) Peter Iamslim (213) 555–6897—ask him to tell Milt Saul and Steve Rose
2) Marty Loomis (818) 555–9333
3) Amy Fisher (213) 555–7767
4) David Martin (213) 555–3836

5) Donna Brownnell (213) 555–7197

6) Lenny Lemarque (213) 555–9963—ask him to tell Monroe and Alison Pierce

7) Hailey Helonovich (213) 555–1936

8) Sean Donnelly (913) 555–8722

9) Mansy Blerman (818) 555–7878

10) The Wrens (Tarzana Hills)

11) Louellen and Don Jones (213) 555–3972

12) Mr. and Mrs. Margarita to tell Meg Margarita (714) 555–3867

13. Bernie Cohen (213) 555–3788—ask him to tell the teachers at Linda Loma Elementary

14. Joannie Timmons (213) 555–1196

15. Marge Pantissimo (213) 555–9631

16. Juan Martinez (818) 555–9399

17. Linda Dickenson (619) 555–8861 to tell Martine Grey

I LOVE YOU ALL VERY MUCH;
I'M SORRY TO CAUSE YOU THIS
GRIEF,

CANDY

with a "Y."

DEATH BY DROWNING

Leslie Dick

1. SUICIDE: TAKE ONE

Connie parked the car on Waterloo Bridge, facing
south. It was a sunny summer evening. As she was
locking the door and William was getting out on the
pavement side, Connie half saw a young man step
over the horizontal guardrail that runs along the edge
of the bridge. He stood there for a moment, only a
few feet away from William. She was very surprised,
thinking this must be some kind of a joke. As she
looked, he vanished. He had jumped off the bridge. A
momentary pause of disbelief: terrifying. Connie
forced herself to go to the edge and look over.

William and Connie held on to the horizontal rail
as they leaned forward, looking down to the river

below. The young man was bobbing about in the water.

Connie was relieved he was alive. Leaning over, she waved, calling out to him, Are you all right? He looked Chinese, maybe twenty-five years old; he shouted out to Connie and William, I FEEL MUCH BETTER NOW. He was waving to them, he seemed elated, very excited. Connie and William were laughing, very pleased; they were laughing with him, and making gestures of triumph and survival. Connie shouted that he must swim to the Embankment, he mustn't swallow any water, she was smiling, with no sense of real danger. This wasn't an emergency, more like some absurd adventure.

Huge sightseeing boats plowed past. The man in the water began to drift downstream. Connie scanned the river's banks and saw the flight of stairs that runs down from the Embankment on the south side of the river to the level of the water. She pointed to it, pointing it out to him, shouting to him to head for those stairs. Everything was all right now. She picked up the pair of worn-out trainers and the red sweatshirt which he had left folded on the bridge; she was going to put them by the stairs for him. Connie and William were laughing and waving to the man in the water. They were all three elated and relieved.

As they started to walk toward the South Bank, Connie saw that the man in the water was having some difficulty swimming. She knew there are treacherous currents in the river. She immediately started to run as fast as she could, to get to a telephone. The sense of relief changed into extreme anxiety.

Running fast, she glanced toward the river; she saw that the man in the water was being carried away downstream. He was moving toward a large metal drum or buoy that floated in the middle of the river. Maybe he could hang on to that, Connie thought, until the river police came to pull him out. As she ran down the steps towards the National Theatre, Connie's last sight of him was some way beyond the drum. She saw his arms wave above his head, like in the poem, and knew he was drowning.

Moving very fast, she went into the National Theatre box office, to make them call 999. She was vehement, insistent. There was some delay, maybe half a minute, because all the telephones were occupied, even the pay phones. This was terrible. When she was sure they'd dialed 999, she ran outside again onto the embankment.

She saw a river police launch silently circling around in the water just downstream from the metal drum. They were looking for the man in the water. Connie realized he was dead.

2. SUICIDE: TAKE TWO

That afternoon, William had a meeting in town, so they arranged to meet at the ICA, around six or six-fifteen. There was an opening of an exhibition, on architecture, at the ICA, and then afterwards they would go on to meet Edith, and Ruby, and other friends, at the NFT bar, south of the river. They were supposed to be going to Steve's performance, to this avant-garde circus Steve was performing in.

Connie always found it disorienting to change, to dress to go out, at five o'clock, but she'd been to Paris a couple of weeks before, and she'd bought the most beautiful jacket, on sale of course, and she wanted to wear it. She wore her new earrings, clips that resembled crinkled nuggets of ore, crumpled silver foil. They were the other major acquisition of the summer. She put on her striped trousers, indulging a fantasy that the boned and padded pale pink jacket in combination with the baggy striped trousers would recall a Regency dandy, would call this to mind, like a rhyme, a shadow, some kind of echo of *dandyisme*. This idea amused her immensely, since she was at the same time convinced that no one else would see it.

Dressed, she felt slightly more prepared for the scrutiny of the crowds. It was like putting on armour, constructing an image that would impress and seduce, surprise and delight. Again, this idea, this fantasy of being looked at, amused Connie (as she got into the car, gingerly, avoiding the grime), it amused her because she was convinced that no one would see her, see it, that way.

The ICA was packed. William arrived at almost exactly the same moment, they found each other near the door. His meeting had gone well; he was very excited, it looked like one of his many projects might come off. Connie thought he was being more than a bit over-optimistic, and slightly resented being positioned as the voice of reason, or doom. She felt her body soaking up the pressure of William's wishful thinking, but they agreed to discuss it later, and plunged into the throng. One of the exhibits in the ICA show was by the architect who was working with William on an exhibition project. Connie had never met him. Shortly, she found herself standing very straight and still while William talked to this extremely highly regarded, very fashionably dressed, famous young architect. His name was Roland Nicholson. She felt stiff, standing very straight in her new jacket, very much on display. She had nothing to say. The architect's model for the new King's Cross was sublime: it was like a kid's model railway gone completely haywire, with canals and gasometers jostling blocks of flats and giant railway signals and trees and highways. It was great; nevertheless, Connie had nothing to say.

It was partly that the room was so very crowded, everyone too close to each other, moving in different directions. It was too hot, too noisy, and the white light was very bright. The line between feeling on display, and feeling painfully exposed, in the glare of noise and light, was slowly being erased. As so often, Connie found herself wishing herself elsewhere.

A woman she'd known for aeons appeared amid the throngs with her new boyfriend in tow. They were both brilliant young architects. The boyfriend didn't acknowledge Connie at all. Connie moved from an initial reaction of paranoia (he doesn't like me) to annoyance. Meanwhile she was introducing Dido to Roland Nicholson, and Dido was being extremely emphatic about something to do with shit, undoubtedly making an impression. She couldn't follow what Dido was saying. She wanted to get out of this crowded noisy place, where as always at openings there were far too many people to be able to see the work, and where anyone could appear at any time, suddenly, unexpectedly, and she'd have to somehow cope with a sudden meeting, absorbing or fending off the psychic collision.

There were times when Connie felt not only vulnerable, times when it was more like feeling flayed, and all the amazing jackets, and subtle, understated earrings, and comic, even witty striped trousers couldn't cover her up. She felt the whole surface of her body to be fragile, easily bruised or cracked, and her hold on language tenuous. Anxiety spread through her body, crumbling away behind the careful façade. It was creeping through the evening, an anxiety she tried to dispel with glasses of red wine. She couldn't make out what anyone was saying. She went on standing there, clutching her wineglass, looking at the crazed model of King's Cross.

Finally they agreed to leave. Getting into the car, William and Connie were openly affectionate with each other. They drove around Trafalgar Square with some difficulty, and headed east along the Strand. Still a little jumpy, Connie wasn't sure if this was the best route to take. William didn't drive, and they often had tiny arguments about better and worse routes. As she was diverted in another circle around the Aldwych and back, William asked about the performance. He had strong views on circuses.

As they turned to head south on Waterloo Bridge, the bright sky opened up wide over their heads, with the expanse of the city spread out on either side. It was a Wednesday evening in early August, the sun was shining, long low beams of yellow light, with the blue sky floating high above. It would be light until nine at night.

Connie parked the car on the left, facing south, half-way across the bridge. There was a small delay, getting out of the car, as Connie reapplied her red lipstick in the rear-view mirror. It was about half-past seven, and as Connie was locking the door on her side, William getting out on his, she half saw a man step over the guardrail that ran along the edge of the bridge. She was surprised, and perplexed: this didn't make sense. Was it a joke? Rag week? As she froze, her look widened, peripherally, to take in the other kids, students (she half thought) that would be with this man, larking about somehow. He was alone.

The young man stood there for a moment, facing out, towards the river, and then he vanished. She saw him drop out of sight. Or perhaps that's wrong, he fell so quickly it was more like she knew he had dropped out of sight. But this didn't make sense either. The young man vanished. With difficulty Connie understood that he had fallen, he had dropped, he had jumped off the bridge.

That moment of difficulty was also a moment of horror: a mixture of fear and disbelief. It paralysed her completely. She forced herself to overcome this resistance; she moved toward the rail. Within the moment of hesitation lay Connie's research into methods of suicide, her knowledge that when someone jumps off the Golden Gate Bridge, for example, or the Brooklyn Bridge, the velocity of their fall, given the height of the bridge, is so great that hitting the surface of the water is like landing on concrete. It is the fall that kills, not drowning. Believing this, Connie was terrified to look over the edge, reluctant to look at death itself. She said to William, "You're killed instantly when you jump."

Together they moved forward and, leaning against the rail, they looked down into the river below. The relief was like a drug, icy and clear, ripping through her body, along her nerves, blowing through her like cold air. The man was bobbing about in the water. Both William and Connie found themselves laughing, smiling uncontrollably. They waved to him, leaning over, looking down into the water, and Connie shouted, "Are you all right?" Seeing the man looked Chinese, maybe, she imagined that perhaps he didn't speak English. The answer came back, shouted from the river water – an ironic answer that seemed to be replete with implication, a whole narrative, a history, contained in its few words, it seemed – the answer came: I FEEL MUCH BETTER NOW.

To Connie, this sentence confirmed that what she had witnessed was a suicide attempt. Like her, reluctant in the moment of horror, terrified to meet the sight of death and then forcing herself to look, like her, this man too had expected death. He had intended to die. Now he was alive, suddenly, and feeling better, wanting to live. He'd changed his mind. A tragedy had turned into a lark, an adventure, a foolish act: swimming in the middle of the Thames.

When she was sixteen, Connie lived for a summer on the river at Battersea, on a Thames barge that was moored at the bottom of an overgrown churchyard. It was not a houseboat, but a nineteenth-century sailing barge that never sailed; it floated up and down on the tide, settling onto the river mud twice a day. She'd lived there with her sister, after the split, when they left their mother's house. The church was by Wren, and William Blake got married in it, and Benedict Arnold, the traitor, was buried in the churchyard. That summer Connie got to know the river, the wide open space of reflected light, the expanse of water smooth under the wide sky, so quiet in the middle of the city, and she got to know the river police. She used to wake up with the changing tide before dawn, and creep up the ladder to perch on the deck, wrapped in Hilary's thick pink shawl. Sitting half out of the hatch near the bow, watching the light on the river endlessly moving, the river police, or fuzz, would appear, checking her out for drugs or something, no doubt. And Connie would give them cups of tea, disarmingly, and they'd tell her about the river.

This is what she remembered: there are treacherous currents, and the water's so poisoned you have to have your stomach pumped out if you fall in.

Leaning over the rail, she shouted to the man in the

river, "Don't swallow the water!" Nevertheless, none of them sensed the danger. They continued to laugh, and wave, making gestures of triumph and survival. Connie could swim well, she was a strong swimmer. William couldn't swim at all. It was impossible for them to judge how difficult it was to swim in the river.

Looking up, Connie quickly scanned the grey stone embankments on either side of the broad river, and saw the steps that descend from the esplanade outside the National Theatre to the level of the water. Somewhere in her mind was a vague idea of avoiding the police, an idea left over from the past – keep the police out of it, if it's not absolutely necessary. At the bottom of this was a notion that they would punish the poor bloke for jumping off the bridge.

Connie pointed to the steps, pointing them out to him, imagining that the man in the river, like Mao in the Yangtse Kiang, would swim across to these steps, cutting through the water, avoiding the barges and power boats and pleasure steamers and all the rest of the river traffic. He would swim across the river to the steps, and climb out, she imagined. He would be OK. Connie and William started to walk toward the South Bank.

Connie picked up the man's trainers and red sweatshirt. The sweatshirt was very faded and worn, and very clean. It was neatly folded on the ground just at the point where he'd stepped over the guardrail. The running shoes were white, and very worn out, with the back of each shoe crumpled, as if they'd been worn as slippers. The pair of shoes, placed side by side on the pavement, next to the folded sweatshirt, seemed imbued with pathos.

Connie's uncle and aunt lived near Seven Sisters, the chalky cliffs on the south coast near Beachy Head, and they'd told her years before that the people who commit suicide from those cliffs always take their shoes off before jumping – as if they were going swimming. They always take off their shoes, and sometimes their coats or jackets, and leave them behind, carefully folded, but the women apparently always hold on to their handbags when they jump.

Connie didn't really want to bring the sweatshirt and shoes, she didn't want to get involved. She wanted to walk away into the sunny evening, laughing with William about their fears and their subsequent elated relief. She wanted to get to the bar and meet her friends. But the practical side weighed heavily: the man in the river would be cold and wet when he got out of the water; so poor, he would need his shoes, his clean sweatshirt.

This sudden momentary resistance, this reluctance to get involved, was real, intransigent, like the fierce hesitation she felt in the first moments after he jumped, the wish not to look, or know, that shock of disbelief and denial. These seemed to be irreducible elements in witnessing a drama or a sudden scene of violence. It was always hard to know how to take part, to measure the correct degree of detachment and help. Connie compromised; she would take the shoes and the sweatshirt, and leave them for the man to find when he climbed out of the water. Connie had no intention of meeting him, or waiting for him to emerge, soaked through and happy, in shock. Hanging around to help seemed too close to a kind of morbid fascination. They were beginning to be late, anyway.

There was this moment, then, that took the place of their initial terror, and their subsequent relieved elation, a moment of calm, almost retrospective, as Connie and William turned away from the railing, to walk toward the South Bank, turning toward each other for the first time, as if to say, phew! what a scene! The evening sunlight filled the air around them, wide blue sky over the wide river, and they were laughing – so very pleased he was all right – and Connie was holding the folded red sweatshirt and the worn pair

of trainers on top of it.

Connie was immensely pleased and also amazed that he was all right, and part of this was merely symbolic, as if the young man in the river reflected or represented something to her, something of herself, over and above his existence as a separate person, with a history and a logic completely unknown to her. In some sense, his survival stood in for her own will to die, and the simultaneous contradictory will to live.

Holding these clothes, Connie tried to imagine his predicament. Maybe he was a student, from Hong Kong, Asia, far from home and family, unbearably lonely, with no one to turn to. A foreigner, she thought – as if being a foreigner in London is enough to drive you to suicide. Maybe he was a homeless person, living in the parking areas under the South Bank where the kids used to skateboard, maybe he was homeless, and penniless, and unable to see a way out. His shoes evinced complete destitution: the soles were worn smooth, there were large holes in the nylon fabric, and their backs were worn down. Connie imagined the Chinese man walking all over the city, walking constantly, too poor to do anything but walk all the time. The red sweatshirt was soft and thin, it was so old, but it was terribly clean. She didn't know how you could keep so clean if you were so poor. Maybe he was crazy, not homeless, maybe he walked his shoes to death compulsively, maniacally. His statement, I FEEL MUCH BETTER NOW, didn't sound crazy, but Connie knew from experience, the experience of her suicidal friends and relations, Connie knew how crazed people get before attempting suicide, and how lucid they become afterwards, as if the act could save you from yourself, or as if your craziness, the craziness itself would fall away, shattered and broken by this sudden collision with possible death. As if the act of violence could always draw a line, stop the craziness, put a limit to it.

Walking across the bridge, smiling at each other, this moment, this interval of equilibrium and contemplation, was exceedingly short. As they walked, Connie looked out over the river and saw that the man was having some difficulty swimming. Without hesitation she immediately began to run as fast as she could. It was essential to get to a phone, to get hold of the river police, get them to pull him out of the water. Her estimation of the situation turned inside out in one moment: it was very very dangerous.

She moved completely independently, shouting something to William as she ran. To convey her sense of danger, difficulty, she shouted, "The water's very cold, it's very cold in the water." Connie thought the fact that William couldn't swim meant he couldn't judge the extent of the danger, or know what was the correct thing to do. She continued running fast, clutching the clothes, unconsciously.

As Connie moved, running, she looked and saw that the man in the water was being carried away downstream. He was only a little bit closer to the river's edge; clearly the currents were very strong. He was moving towards a large metal drum that floated in the middle of the river. Connie hoped he could hang on to it, until the river police came to haul him out. She imagined a chain or a big rusty ring on the incomprehensible drum or buoy, and him hanging on to it as the huge river poured past, pulling at his body. Maybe he could hold on, against the pull of the tide. She continued to run very fast.

Reaching the steps that went down to the National Theatre, in a glance Connie saw the man was very near the drum, on the far side of it. She hoped that was where the chain or ring would be. As she ran down the steps she looked up again and saw him some way beyond the drum. Without stopping, Connie looked up and out, she saw him, her eyes found him in the water. She saw his arms waving above his head. She had never seen that before, that "not waving but drowning" gesture, both arms raised and flailing. She knew he was drowning.

Connie rushed into the National Theatre box-office, her voice very shrill, cutting through the air full of fragmented conversations, a thick mesh of sounds and words. Some people were buying tickets, or reading the programmes, and three people were behind the counter, all on the telephone. "Please can you call 999, there's a man in the river, please, call 999," she kept saying, over and over, amazed that they didn't immediately interrupt their conversations, cut them off, to dial 999. She was frantic, moving around the small space, back and forth. She couldn't understand these oblivious people: did someone drown in the river every day? Vehement, insistent, Connie raised her voice to penetrate the layers of cross-talk. As she heard the young woman say into the telephone, "I really must go, but will I see you later?", Connie moved to see if there was a payphone free. Two people sat on seats in little cubicles, talking.

This nightmare lasted moments, an intolerable delay. When Connie saw that the young woman was dialling 999, she ran outside again.

As Connie came out of the entrance, she faced an expanse of pavement extending to the stone wall that ran along the embankment, the edge of the river. Running across, she saw some people leaning against this wall, people standing there, looking at the river. There was a line of people standing along the bridge, also; she took them in for the first time. What was this, a spectacle? She ran straight toward the river. When she reached the wall of the embankment, she continued running downstream, speaking sideways to

William, who was right beside her. "Where is he?" she said. Connie was still holding the red sweatshirt and the trainers against her chest. She was completely unaware of this. They paused for a moment and a man spoke to them; he told them that he'd telephoned the police, "as soon as he jumped." The river was smooth, her eyes scanning, she couldn't find the little figure, distant, she couldn't find the dark shape of his head breaking the smooth metallic surface of the moving water. She saw a river police launch silently circling around a little way downstream from the metal drum. Connie realized he was dead.

Connie placed the red sweatshirt and the trainers on the broad stone wall. Turning away, she burst into uncontrollable, explosive tears and loud crying. She was telling William he was dead, drowned; William couldn't believe it. She was overwhelmed with acute grief for this unknown person, this living thing now dead. Connie saw the clothes and shoes on the wall and picked them up. She was crying so much that people were looking at her. She put the clothes down on a wooden bench, and sat down beside them, holding her face in her hands. Her mouth wide open, she sobbed, wailing.

She said, "You drown in three minutes." She repeated this over and over again. It was to persuade William it was true. She had a violent impulse to tear off her beautiful jacket, her ridiculous expensive lovely jacket, and her new earrings, and throw them into the river – as if this sacrifice could bring him back. That's how she formulated it; she felt she would do anything to bring him back.

For the first time the thought struck her that she should have jumped into the river and saved him. She was a strong swimmer. She should have jumped in and saved him, immediately. She turned to William, to tell him this, and together, through her tears, they carefully constructed a justification: No, she shouldn't have jumped into the river, because she could have hurt herself, she could have drowned, she didn't know how to rescue people in big rivers, and anyway, he'd seemed to be OK.

They repeated this, they kept telling each other, reminding each other that he seemed to be OK. William said, "There's nothing more we could have done."

A man came up to them, enquiring. He'd seen the guy jump, he'd gone in to get a drink. Bitterly, Connie said, "He's dead." The man's response was total disbelief: "He can't be, he was swimming, he looked like he was all right." Connie said, "No, he drowned. You drown in three minutes." She said it like an accusation, as if she were accusing everyone else of not knowing how easy it is to drown, speaking out her own self-accusation.

Maybe he'd broken something, his arm, maybe, when he hit the water. Maybe he didn't realize, no one realized.

Somewhere in this confusion, Connie was very glad to know that someone else had phoned the police the minute it happened. She stood up, turning her back on the wide river. She was still crying like crazy. William seemed numb, standing there beside her. Another stranger, surprised by her tears, said, "What, did you know him?" – as if that would be the only reason to be so upset. "No!" she said, walking away.

They sat down again further away, on a round piece of stone, like a big grindstone lying flat on the ground. It appeared to be the detritus from some live sculpture event, a South Bank watch-the-artist display. Connie and William were at a loss; they didn't know what to do. Connie went on crying, like an emotional explosion that didn't stop. It was as if she were grieving for all the people who want to do themselves in and then suddenly don't, who change their minds, who want to live, to be rescued or somehow to survive, and who don't make it, by some chance, some malign circumstance. "He wanted to live," she said to William.

The man who'd telephoned the police right away approached them, carrying the red sweatshirt and the shoes. He said, "I don't want to intrude . . ." Connie wiped her face with her hands, wet with tears and snot, unable to look up. The man said, "Are these his clothes?" He mentioned the police and Connie imagined having to give a statement to the police, she said, "I don't want to talk to the cops, I won't talk to them." The man said that was OK, he would talk to them, he'd give them the clothes. So William and Connie told him what they knew, speaking at the same time, Connie crying but trying to be clear and straightforward. She said, "He changed his mind. He said, *I feel much better now.* He wanted to live." The man listened carefully, without comment.

It's not possible to mourn the loss of someone you don't know, Connie thought. He can only represent something of yourself to you, he stands in for your own suicide fantasies, your own wish to live. But much more shocking than this, more pressing than the displaced enactment of her own destructive wish, was the simple fact of death: unbelievable.

One moment he was there, the next he was gone. The appropriate word was "gone"; she wanted to "bring him back". The transparent fabric of everyday life was torn through, ripped open, to disclose the constant dark presence, the proximity of death. "In the midst of life we are in death," Connie said. It was inconceivable.

Connie and William didn't know what to do. Connie'd agreed with Edith to meet at seven-thirty or eight, in the NFT bar; she remembered saying they'd be there by eight-thirty at the latest. The circus began at nine. She knew she didn't want to go to the circus, now, but she felt she had to go to the bar, if only to tell Edith that she wasn't coming, so they wouldn't wait. Connie and William explained this to each other, and then William said, "Let's get a drink, anyway."

Her face wet, still encased in the absurd masquerade of high fashion, red lipstick, earrings, Connie stumbled into the NFT. She felt it was like having a great hole cut in your chest, a great gash through your body, and still being able to walk, talk. One minute he was there, bobbing about in the water, shouting to them, laughing; the next he was dead – gone, absent, lost forever. Nonexistent. She couldn't get over it; she couldn't take it in. It happened so quickly. It was so sudden. She felt like there was a black hole cut in her chest.

Connie paused near the door, reluctant to penetrate the crowded bar any further. Standing there, Ruby appeared, alone, and Connie took hold of her and told her what had happened. She started to cry again. Ruby said, "Oh Con, how awful, how dreadful, come in, come in and have a drink."

Then Edith came up, and Connie found herself telling her the story, it was beginning to take form, a story, and Edith was very sympathetic. It was

extremely difficult to tell this tale, to give it shape, to bring her shock and the violence of this unknown death to the crowded bar, the group of friends. Edith got her a drink, red wine, and William started downing glasses of rum. It seemed OK, for the time being, to stand there, with her friends, drinking. Robert arrived, her old boyfriend, and she told him about it. He was fantastic, he listened carefully and took it all in, and then without a break he was talking about other things, being normal, and so was Connie, back into life. Talking with him, Connie would abruptly return to the death, and Robert would listen, and then he would carry on about something else. He even made her laugh, her face shiny with dried tears, her mouth pulled out of shape from crying.

It was hard to know what to do, to guess what the right thing to do would be. For a time, standing in the bar surrounded by these friends, talking, drinking, seemed to be the right thing to do. At eight-thirty they all trooped off to Jubilee Gardens, to the circus, and Connie and William climbed the steps up to the bridge, to get in the car and drive home. The river was deep silvery blue, the surface of the water like pewter reflecting the darkening blue of the sky, and the city looked beautiful, outlined in black and grey with all the different lights shining.

At home they ate scrambled eggs on toast and went to bed. Recalling the view of the river, the brilliant city, it was impossible to believe he would never see it again.

3. SUICIDE: TAKE THREE

The first suicide that penetrated Connie's world was Marilyn Monroe's suicide in 1962. Connie was seven; she asked her mother what it meant, to commit suicide. Her mother, typically, gave the impression of being slightly annoyed to be asked a difficult question. She said it was when people jump out of the window, when people jump off the roof, when they jump out of tall buildings. It was as if her mother were trying to present a harmless image of suicide, and came up with a stereotype from cartoons in *The New Yorker*, the banker or industrialist ridiculous on the window ledge, the Crash.

They lived in Chicago then, and there were lots of tall buildings around. It was easy to imagine jumping out the window of one of them. For some years after, Connie associated the death of Marilyn Monroe with this image of sudden, slow falling, this skyscraper death.

Later, when Connie knew how Monroe really died, people said that she'd changed her mind, Marilyn Monroe had taken all these pills and then she'd decided she didn't want to die after all but by then it was too late. Of course, you couldn't change your mind if you jumped off a tall building.

People argued over whether Sylvia Plath had wanted or expected to be rescued when she put her head in the oven, or whether she'd planned it carefully, timing it so the au pair would show up and the kids wouldn't be alone with no one to look after them. As it happened, the au pair couldn't get into the flat, because the man who lived downstairs who had the extra key had been drugged by the gas seeping through the kitchen floor above, and didn't wake up when she knocked. This would seem to imply rather a large quantity of gas, and the possibility of Plath being revived appears unlikely.

Connie remembered the hot summer day when she went swimming with friends in Sussex, in the River Ouse, near where Virginia Woolf committed suicide. The river was very narrow and silty and slow, and she realized Woolf must have very definitely wanted to die, since it wouldn't be easy to drown yourself in such a river. On the other hand, maybe the meandering river had silted up in the thirty-five years since this death. The name of the river was pronounced "ooze," appropriately.

Connie's mother always said, "You drown in three

minutes." She also always said, "You can drown in three inches of water." Met with disbelief, or even the slightest whiff of doubt, Connie's mother would insist: "You can drown in a bathtub with three inches of water in it." Connie grew up with these vehement statistics, repetitions of the number three, echoing through her childhood. It was the voice of maternal anxiety translated into violent assertion and, finally, threat. Like Connie's mother was always obsessed, it seemed, with the point of a pencil, how it would go in your eye if you ran with it and fell,—or through the roof of your mouth. You mustn't suck a pen or a pencil, or walk with it in your mouth, because you might trip and fall and it would go through the roof of your mouth. You must always hold scissors pointing toward the ground, and walk, not run, when you were holding them.

You must never point a gun at anyone, a toy gun, any kind of gun, because you never know what might happen.

Connie's mother made a habit at one point of giving expensive scissor and paper-knife sets in leather cases to her friends, as Christmas or birthday presents, but she would always make each of them give her a penny or some small coin first, so that technically it wasn't a gift, it was a purchase, like the friend was buying them from her. Because to give someone scissors or a knife implies a wish to cut them, or hurt them somehow. A gift is always a prediction, some kind of wish for the future, like a spell.

Thus everyday objects became a potential source of

extreme violence. Connie's mother would also, more rarely, describe how any sharp object, even something as innocuous as a pencil, could conceivably be used as a weapon if a strange man was attacking you. You could stab him in the throat, for example, with the sharp point of a pencil. Or in the eye. These vivid images reappeared in Connie's dreams years later, glimpses of torn throats and ordinary lead pencils that somehow emanated a vast and uncontainable horror. Thinking about her mother's advice, Connie decided that trying to stab an assailant with a pencil in the throat would probably only infuriate him, and possibly elicit further violence in retaliation. Generally speaking, Connie tended to believe she'd be able to talk her way out of any situation—like she'd talked her way out of being raped by the guy who picked her up hitchhiking that night, the last time she ever hitched a lift—although she knew that belief was unrealistic.

A couple of years before, Connie had decided to study self-defense. She had come to the realization that she was fundamentally physically frightened of men. This was such a normal part of everyday life she wasn't even aware of it, but it crossed her mind that perhaps it wasn't inevitable, maybe she could learn how not to be frightened, maybe this could change things in some way for her. During the third meeting, the self-defense teacher, a laughing thin young woman who enthusiastically demonstrated the power of Chi energy, taught them how to kill someone.

Connie didn't go back again: the class was at an inconvenient time, it was too far away. Later she recognized that she really didn't want to know how to kill someone, even a rapist. She'd wanted to learn how to defend herself. It wasn't a very effective method of killing someone anyway, it would only really be viable if the man was asleep or something, and wasn't fighting back. In New York a while later, Connie was telling this story and a woman friend said exactly the same thing had happened to her. You take up self-defense, you're taught how to kill somebody in the third session, and you never go back. You don't want to know.

Some time later William told Connie that he'd been completely flummoxed by the scene on the bridge, as if he couldn't understand it, he couldn't take it in. Connie was fascinated to discover differences in their recollections and understanding of what happened, although at the time she'd known that the question of being able or unable to swim must make a difference. For example, being unable to swim, William had immediately looked around the bridge for some kind of lifejacket or ring to throw into the water. Connie was impressed; she hadn't thought of doing that. He'd even looked for a telephone on the bridge, an emergency phone; he told Connie about the phone on the Brooklyn Bridge, mysteriously placed just beside the walkway where a suicidal pedestrian could clamber over the fence to get to the edge and jump off. As if you would ring up and tell them you were about to do it, as if there would be a whole apparatus of rescue that would come into operation if you saw someone about to jump and made the call.

There was no such apparatus here, and meanwhile Connie, the swimmer, had mistakenly imagined that the man in the water, swimming, would be all right. William never contradicted this misperception, partly, he told Connie, because he didn't know anything about swimming, and partly because being able to swim seemed to be this guy's only hope.

William told Connie he'd been very shocked by the man's age, but then he thought the man was younger than Connie did, he thought he was about eighteen or nineteen, whereas Connie thought he might be twenty-four or twenty-five. William agreed, eventually, commenting that Chinese people often look younger than they are. Still he expressed surprise that someone so young should want to kill himself, though he knew that young people bump themselves off all the time. Maybe more kids kill themselves than older people, who knows. The combination of the guy looking so young and being Chinese made the death even more incomprehensible to him.

William said, "That was the other thing I thought was strange; it seemed strange to me that a Chinese person would choose to commit suicide in that way. I mean, I somehow think of jumping off bridges as being terribly English, a terribly English way to do it."

Connie didn't feel this way at all; bridges were simply a very cheap and available method, unlike most others, which require some kind of weapon or poison. Bridges were free.

Connie recalled an item she'd read in the evening

paper years before, in the *Evening Argus*, about an Indian woman, wearing a sari, who walked into a butcher's shop in Hove and took one of the very large, very sharp butcher's knives and cut her throat on the spot. Connie pictured the collision, what her friend Iris used to call cognitive dissonance: the round pink faces and burly shoulders of the butchers, so very English, blood smears on their white jackets, and then this young Indian woman, her sari bright against the shiny glass counters and white tiled walls of the shop. Bloody meat laid out in stainless-steel trays, every surface wiped clean and shining, this scene of carefully controlled horror invaded without warning by an even more controlled and sudden death. The newspaper didn't speculate on the woman's motives, as if she were completely unknowable, completely opaque: foreign. Connie read the scene as enacting a last-ditch protest against being treated like an animal, to be slaughtered by butchers, but it may simply have been that the woman had no money, and the knives in the butcher's are very sharp and they're free.

Thinking about Englishness, suicide and jumping from bridges, Connie recalled the plaque on Hammersmith Bridge, which she'd discovered by chance when she was about sixteen and very romantic, deeply preoccupied by Keats and Shelley and dying. It is a brass plaque set into the heavy mahogany railing that runs along the bridge, a railing worn smooth by a hundred years of people leaning against it, or running their hands along it as they crossed the river. It commemorates the death of a soldier who heroically jumped into the icy river at midnight, on a date in December or January somewhere around 1917 or 1918. He jumped into the river in order to save the life of a woman suicide, which he succeeded in doing, but unfortunately died himself. He "lost his life in the attempt."

Connie could picture this scene too: the late dark night, very cold, and the young woman letting herself into the icy water, knowing her skirts would drag her down. Was this an image from Dickens, maybe? *Our Mutual Friend*? Probably not, but it had to come from somewhere, she thought. In this version, Connie didn't allow the woman to jump from the bridge. She walked or slid into the icy water from the bank on the south side, where there was still a long stretch of towpath running beside the wide, smooth river; a ribbon of old trees and untended bushes, thick grass, overgrown, where in the summer lovers walked or lay, and solitary people would sit, watching the river. Freezing cold, now, dark, midwinter: the woman would be young, and thin, a prostitute maybe, or a housemaid, pregnant, in despair (what book was this taken from?) and longing for death. The young officer on the bridge, his heavy overcoat wrapped tight around him against the cold, the young officer would not hesitate; hearing her inadvertent cry, he would plunge in.

Connie elaborated: he was on leave from the trenches, disillusioned necessarily by the horrors of that war yet somehow retaining a crazed ideal of valor or heroism, some idea of what it was the young men were so endlessly dying to defend, something of value, something possibly symbolized by English woman-hood. When Lytton Strachey's claim to the status of conscientious objector was contested, he was asked in court, "And what would you do if you saw a German soldier attempting to rape your sister?" With only the slightest whiff of irony, Strachey replied, "I should try and interpose my own body."

If that was the question, the rape of sisters and how to defend them, then, seeing a woman at midnight in the icy Thames, he wouldn't hesitate. And she would live, and he would die—of what? Exposure, or drowning? Connie couldn't remember. Maybe at an unconscious level he'd wanted to die, maybe he'd had enough of death, too much. More people died in the great influenza epidemic of 1918 than were killed in the war itself. It was the guilt of the survivor; the war over, they dropped like flies. There was the sleeping sickness epidemic around that time too. Connie pictured the whole of Europe in shock, unable to take in the extent of the damage, the deaths, unable to contain the grief, and therefore going to sleep, or dying of flu, some kind of collective self-sacrifice. That's what the scene on the bridge was, the scene on Hammersmith Bridge in 1918, a scene of self-sacrifice, for an unknown object, the anonymous woman. Connie wondered if she'd eventually succeeded in doing herself in, later.

Returning to William, Connie didn't think of jumping off bridges as particularly English. She remembered how she'd pored over Warhol's disaster paintings, the *New York Post* photos of falling bodies;

she remembered the great big bridges of America, the Golden Gate, the Brooklyn Bridge, the bridge to Terminal Island. English bridges, or London bridges, were too low for a foolproof suicide, as the scene with the Chinese man on Waterloo Bridge demonstrated. You weren't even knocked out by the collision with the surface of the water, you weren't pulverized like you were supposed to be when you jumped off a really big bridge. You had to drown, but then it wasn't that difficult to drown, it seems.

Connie thought of drowning more as a specifically female mode of suicide, partly because of Ophelia, and her dress, which begins by buoying her up, and later pulls her down to the bottom of the river. Adolescent, Connie would study Millais's painting of Ophelia in the river, fascinated by her friend Ruby's story of how the model, Lizzie Siddal, died of pneumonia after posing for the painting, lying in a zinc bathtub of freezing water hour after hour. Later she found out this wasn't true.

Shelley's first wife, Harriet Westbrook, killed herself at the age of twenty-two by jumping from the bridge across the Serpentine—an amazing feat, considering the little, almost ornamental bridge of white stone can't be more than twenty feet above the lake. It's the bridge where Mrs. Dalloway threw a sixpence into the water, one moonlit night; it was another of Connie's favorite views of the city, a view with trees over water. Which is one reason why she remembered so vividly about Shelley's first wife. He'd run off with Mary Godwin, who was about seventeen; she was pregnant, and they'd gone to Switzerland, and then to Italy, with Byron, and Claire Clairmont, who was Mary's stepsister. Claire was madly in love with Byron, and also pregnant. Mary Godwin's first child died within ten days of its birth; she became pregnant again almost immediately. In the autumn of 1816, her half sister, Fanny Imlay, Mary Wollstonecraft's other daughter, committed suicide; she took laudanum in a run-down Swansea hotel. Then, in December, they received news of the suicide of Shelley's wife, Harriet, drowned in the Serpentine late one night after jumping from the bridge, eight and a half months pregnant with another man's child. All the babies died, or miscarried, and Mary sat down and wrote *Frankenstein*.

Sylvia Plath put glasses of milk beside her children's beds. Virginia Woolf put stones in the pockets of her long cardigan, to weigh her body down. Harriet Shelley had a baby inside her. It's not difficult to drown if you cannot swim.

Unable to swim, William had no real sense of this danger; not unlike Connie imagining she could talk her way out of anything, even rape, William vaguely took it for granted that he would inexplicably suddenly be able to swim, in an emergency, if he would otherwise drown. Connie found herself returning over and over to fearful thoughts of William's death. She imagined being in the water, the vast, deep ocean, with him, and telling him how to keep his head above water, teaching him to tread water as they waited to be rescued. She wondered if she'd be able to hold his head above the water, to keep him floating beside her there.

This was an absurd image: Connie teaching William how to float, after they've somehow found themselves in the ocean, after their boat has capsized, their plane crashed? Maybe it was reasonable, maybe if someone you love can't swim, you can't help anticipating, imagining what you'd do if you found yourselves at sea. It was part of the role reversal syndrome, that she should be plagued by fantasies of saving him, and he should be calmly unaware, oblivious to the danger, either real or fantasized, and, it seemed, totally unconcerned with any idea of saving her. William liked her precisely because she could look after herself. He was irritated by her fear of flying, because it so obviously contradicted this impression. As it was, they rarely confronted large bodies of water, except to look at them from a distance. You can drown in a bathtub, her mother's doom-laden voice echoed down the years, resounding darkly in the bright day, but no, that wasn't true, maybe babies drown in bathtubs, if you let them slide under, slip out of your grasp, but Connie couldn't imagine William drowning in his daily, ritual morning bath.

Thinking about it, Connie concluded that she should have encouraged the man who died, the Chinese man in the river, she should have encouraged him to stay put, to tread water, to let his body float. She should have told him to wait to be picked up, to relax and be patient, instead of pointing to the distant steps and saying, swim over there! It was too far to swim, she should have realized; he jumped at the exact center of the bridge, and the river was so wide there, a great smooth expanse of moving water. One of them should have stayed with him, talking to him and encouraging him to keep his head above water, to relax, while the other immediately got hold of the police. Probably the fastest way to do that would be to stop a cab with a radio, and get the driver to call. Like using a CB network, use the radio cab. Faster than running to one end of the bridge or the other.

If they'd done that, the river still would have carried the man away, moving downstream, but maybe he wouldn't have become so exhausted, if that was what killed him. Connie really didn't know what killed him, when he wanted to live so much. I FEEL MUCH BETTER NOW. He was laughing about it, waving his fist in the air, defiantly. Connie imagined it must have been a combination of exhaustion, not being able to swim very well, maybe a broken bone or two, and the treacherous currents and icy cold water of the river that killed him.

4. SUICIDE: TAKE FOUR

Remembering the suicide, Connie realized the man in the river had met death twice. First the sudden fall, plunging straight into the endless water, rushing deep, away from the light. And then reaching the point, immeasurable, where the descent slows, and stops, the gentle recoil, as the heavy cold water begins to push the narrow body up again. Moving slowly, and then faster, rising to break the surface: air, light, sounds. Not dead after all: elation.

And then the second death—drifting, lost. The pull of the water, the shock, exhaustion. People watching from a distance, bright sky so wide and high, isolation. Desperate wish for some help, from somewhere, unimaginable, and no help comes. A hand reaching out, something to hang on to. Arms flailing, lost, and being carried away by the river, carried under, to breathe in the icy water at last.

Connie wept, and then she stopped weeping. She made a decision. Thinking about these literary suicides and parasuicides, and later thinking of her own death, her own occasional longing for death, Connie made a rule, she drew a line.

No messing about with death, no inviting death in and then asking him to leave after all. No flirting, no fascination, no razors, no pills, no bridges, no gas. Someone walking in with a cigarette could blow up the whole house. No suicide here, no—no white bandages romantically tied around wrists under black leather sleeves. No livid scars up and down her arms, exposed by the gesture of running fingers through her hair, bright bangles slipping along these scarred arms, no chaotic tracery of razor marks revealed. No stomach pumps at the hospital, no body on the tracks. No ocean, no river, no cliff. None of that.

NOTES ON THE CONTRIBUTORS

Rupert Adley is a poet, fiction writer, and PWA. Originally from London, he now lives in San Francisco.

Neil Bartlett is a director, performer, translator, and writer. He has written *Ready to Catch Him Should He Fall*, a novel, and *Who Was That Man?*, a polemic history. He is a founding member of Gloria, a theater company in London, and his work for theater includes *A Vision of Love Revealed in Sleep*, *Sarrasine*, *A Judgement in Stone*, and *Night After Night*.

Stephen Beachy has published a novel, *The Whistling Song*. His prose has appeared in the 'zines *Mirage #4/Period(ical)*, *coeval*, and *Madonna/Ho*. He lives in Santa Barbara, where he is working on a new novel.

Michael Blumlein is the author of *The Movement of Mountains*, *X, Y*, and *The Brains of Rats*. He has written for both stage and screen, and his newest novel, *Life Gate Fire*, is forthcoming.

Rebecca Brown is the author of *Annie Oakley's Girl*, *The Terrible Girls*, *The Haunted House*, and *The Children's Crusade*. Her new book, *The Gifts of the Body*, is forthcoming in 1994. She lives in Seattle.

Gil Cuadros, a poet and fiction writer, has received

a Brody Arts Fellowship for poetry. He has been published in the anthologies *Indivisible* and *Blood Whispers: L.A. Writers on AIDS*. His work can also be heard on the compact disk *Verdict and the Violence: Poets' Response to the LA Uprising*. He is a PWA living in Los Angeles, where he works with high-risk kids, exposing them to art and the diverse cultures of Southern California.

Leslie Dick is the author of *Kicking* and *Without Falling*. Her stories have appeared in various anthologies, including *The Seven Deadly Sins*, *Sex and the City*, and *Other than Itself: Writing Photography*. She divides her time between London and Los

Angeles, where she teaches at California Institute of the Arts.

Rikki Ducornet is the author of four novels: *The Stain*, *Entering Fire*, *The Fountains of Neptune*, and *The Jade Cabinet*. Her collected fiction, *The Complete Butcher's Tales*, will be published in 1994.

Diamanda Galas is an international vocalist and composer, and directs Intravenal Sound Operations, based in New York and Berlin. Her most recent work, *Insekta*, was performed at The Kitchen and Lincoln Center in New York City in June 1993. Her other performances include *Plague/Mass* and *Vena Cava*. Her recordings are available on Mute/Elektra.

John Giorno has written many books, including *You*

Got to Burn to Shine: Selected Poetry and Prose and *Cancer in My Left Ball*. He has produced twenty-eight LPs, CDs, and tape cassettes on his label, Giorno Poetry Systems, and is the founder of the AIDS Treatment Project.

Craig G. Harris was a poet, journalist, and fiction writer. His work has appeared in *Brother to Brother: New Writings by Black Gay Men; Gay Life; New Men, New Minds; In the Life*; and *Tongues Untied*. He died of AIDS in 1992.

Stewart Home is the author of *The Assault on Culture, Pure Mania*, and *Defiant Prose*. During the 1980s, he was a leading member of the Neoist movement and an organizer of the International Festivals of Plagiarism. He lives in London.

Darius James is the author of *Negrophobia*. His work appears in *The Between C & D Reader* and *Love Is Strange*. He is currently working on a book about blaxploitation films.

Patrick McGrath has written *Dr. Haggard's Disease, Spider, The Grotesque*, and *Blood and Other Tales*. He divides his time between London and New York City.

Akilah Nayo Oliver is a poet and performance artist. Her work has appeared in *Harbinger Poetry Anthology* and *Invocation L.A.: Urban Multicultural Poetry*. She has performed at Beyond Baroque Literary Arts

Center, UCLA, Highways Performance Space, and Watts Towers Arts Center.

Suzette Partido is an ex-San Francisco 'zine-o-phile now living in San Diego and doing prevention and outreach work with at-risk mid-city teens. Her writing has appeared in *Some Weird Sin*, *Discontents*, *Dear World*, and *Crimes Tabloid*.

Darryl Pinckney is the author of *High Cotton*. He has been a Hodder Fellow at Princeton University and a recipient of grants from the Ingram-Merrill and Guggenheim foundations.

362   Kate Pullinger has published a collection of short stories, *Tiny Lies*, and two novels, *When the Monster Dies* and *Where Does Kissing End?* She is the editor of *A Gambling Box*. Originally from Canada, she has lived in London since 1982.

Ann Rower is the author of *If You're a Girl*, a book of stories, and is working on a second collection, called *Armed Response*, about her West Coast family. She lives in New York City, where she teaches at the School of Visual Arts.

Sapphire is the author of *American Dreams*. Her writing has appeared in *Women on Women*, *Critical Condition: Women on the Edge of Violence*, *War After War*, and *Queer City: The Portable Lower East Side*. She lives in New York City.

Benjamin Weissman is an artist and fiction writer. He is the author of *Dear Dead Person*, a book of short fiction. His stories have appeared in *The Village Voice Literary Supplement*, *BOMB*, and *Santa Monica Review*, and he is a regular contributor to *ArtForum*.

John Wynne is the author of *The Other World*, a book of stories, and *Crimewave*, a novel. His work has been anthologized in Calder's *New Writing and Writers*, and his poetry has been featured in *American Poetry Review*, *The Paris Review*, and *Bastard Review*.

ABOUT THE EDITORS

Amy Scholder is an editor at City Lights Books. She recently edited *Critical Condition: Women on the Edge of Violence*, *Memories That Smell Like Gasoline* by David Wojnarowicz and *Jerk* by Nayland Blake and Dennis Cooper. She is a performance/literature curator at The Lab gallery in San Francisco.

Ira Silverberg is a literary agent, book publicist, and associate publisher of Serpent's Tail. He edited *Everything Is Permitted: The Making of Naked Lunch*. He is a contributing editor to *The Portable Lower East Side*, a member of the board of directors of *BOMB* magazine, and cochairman of the PEN Lesbian and Gay Committee.

Scholder and Silverberg edited *HIGH RISK: An Anthology of Forbidden Writings*, and are editors of HIGH RISK Books, an imprint of Serpent's Tail.

PERMISSIONS

"Introduction," by Amy Scholder and Ira Silverberg. Copyright © 1994 by Amy Scholder and Ira Silverberg.

"I'm Going Out Like a Fucking Meteor!" by Craig G. Harris. Copyright © 1994 by the Estate of Craig G. Harris.

"Throwing Shade," by Darryl Pinckney. Copyright © 1994 by Darryl Pinckney.

"Strange Juice," "One Day," by Sapphire have been excerpted from *American Dreams* (HIGH RISK Books/Serpent's Tail, 1994). Copyright © 1994 by Sapphire.

"Morphia," by Patrick McGrath has been excerpted from *Dr. Haggard's Disease* (Poseidon, US; Viking, UK 1993). Copyright © 1993 by Patrick McGrath.

"Confessions of a Girl," by Kate Pullinger has been excerpted from *Where Does Kissing End?* (Serpent's Tail, UK 1993; Random House, US 1995). Copyright © 1994 by Kate Pullinger.

"Hunters/Gatherers," by Stephen Beachy. Copyright © 1994 by Stephen Beachy.

369

Founded in 1986, Serpent's Tail publishes the innovative and the challenging.

If you would like to receive a catalogue of our current publications please write to:

FREEPOST
Serpent's Tail
4 Blackstock Mews
LONDON N4 2BR

(No stamp necessary if your letter is posted in the United Kingdom.)